Lives of Social Insects

Also by
Peggy Pickering Larson
and Mervin W. Larson:

ALL ABOUT ANTS

Peggy Pickering Larson
and Mervin W. Larson

Lives of Social Insects

THE WORLD PUBLISHING COMPANY
New York and Cleveland

Published by the World Publishing Company
2231 West 110th Street, Cleveland, Ohio 44102
Published simultaneously in Canada
by Nelson, Foster & Scott Ltd.

First Printing 1968

Designed by Christine Wilkinson
Library of Congress Catalog Card Number: 68–13711

Printed in the United States of America

To

Corinne and Mike Larson,
Marguerite Pickering,
and in memory of
Leo Pickering

Contents

Introduction: Social Insects

THE ANT HILL, bee hive, and termite nest have often held a fascination for the philosopher. In them he has at times tended to see, mirrored, man's society. For man and social insects—greatly different structurally and behaviorally—are yet strangely, superficially similar in one respect, their social way of life. The biologist too views the ants, bees, wasps, and termites with fascination—not because he sees them in terms of human society but because these social insects are of great interest in their own right. To the biologist the social organization and way of life of the social insects need not—indeed should not—be interpreted in the shadow of man's egocentric viewpoint to be either appreciated or understood.

Social animals are defined as species in which individuals help to care for the young of other individuals of the same species. There are literally thousands of species of insects that have achieved a social way of life. These species, while numerous, are restricted, all of them being included within four main types of insects—termites, wasps, bees, and ants. There are more species of social insects than of all other social animals combined. Man, of course, is the primary species of which we think when we are considering animals that live in societies. Yet the insect societies antedate man's by many millions of years. Whereas it is generally considered that man first began living in true societies within the last million years, there were ants functioning on this level perhaps as much as 100 million years ago, and termites had probably developed their populous, organized cities even before that.

The societies of man and insects are only superficially similar, for they are built upon different bases. The insects, equipped only with instinct and a slight learning ability, have used vast spans of time in evolving their body forms, instincts, and living habits into a social way of life. Their social pattern of living is passed on, more or less intact, from one generation to the next through genetic transmission—that is, the pattern is inherited. Man, on the other hand, has built up a vast culture in conjunction with his social way of life, and as this culture is passed on, it can be expanded with each successive generation. Human society has a cultural transmission; insect societies a genetic transmission. This makes the insect societies no less interesting, for the societies themselves and the factors that organize and regulate them are marvels of complexity, which man is only just beginning to understand.

The definition of a true insect society varies, but basically it includes the ideas that such a society is one in which numbers of a single species of different generations stay together, females help to care for young that are not necessarily their own, and a division of labor exists within the group. Insect societies are in the main based on family relationships in which the mother (or in some instances, both parents) remains with the young. The latter, in turn, also stay in the nest and aid in the rearing of more young, which are ordinarily produced by a single queen-mother.

Among the insects as a whole a great range of habits is found, extending from insects that are solitary to those that are subsocial to those that are truly social. The majority of the insects are solitary, actively associating with others of their species only at mating time. Indeed, there are female insects which can reproduce without even this association. In some cases the male and female, after mating, make some provisions for the welfare of their young but do not ever have contact with them. Finally there are those insects that remain with their young for varying periods of time. These are the subsocial and social species.

Some earwigs, those flat, forceps-tailed creatures that at times run about our flower beds, have reached a subsocial level of living. The female earwigs guard their eggs in an earthen cell and mouth them, evidently thus preventing the growth of fungi on them. The female remains with the young for a period and protects them in their early stages.

Ambrosia beetles also lead a subsocial life. The female of these beetles excavates a tunnel through wood and there she lays her eggs in small niches. Within the tunnel she tends a crop of fungus that grows on a base of wood chips and excrement. This is a pattern that we shall see again among the social insects. In some species the young of the beetle graze on the growth, but in others the mother actually feeds it to them. She remains with the developing young until they have reached maturity; then the group disbands.

A third example of subsocial insects is the embiids, or web spinners. These are small insects that live in colonies within silken tunnels which they spin in debris, under stones, under bark, or in similar locations. The insects are slender, usually ½ inch or less in length, eat plant materials, and have glands on the front legs with which they produce the silk. This arrangement is unlike that of the spiders, which produce silk from spinnerets on the abdomen, or that of the larvae of bees, wasps, and some ants, which produce silk from glands in the mouth. The maze of tunnels spun by a colony of web spinners aids in protecting these strange inhabitants and may also give them some control of temperature and humidity within their quarters. The embiids are unusual in that they can run forward and backward in their narrow tunnels with equal facility. In some cases the silken tunnels are connected to a few subterranean tunnels into which the insects can also retreat. Within her tunnel a female web spinner lays her eggs in a mass. She protects the eggs and for a brief period the young also. Eventually the young begin spinning their own adjacent small tunnels into which they move.

In the following chapters we survey a variety of living patterns developed by the fully social insects. Among these we will note that not only are the young cared for, but most of them remain in the parental nest and help to care for additional generations produced by their mother the queen, or by additional queens. Within this colony a division of labor develops. This division is made possible by the fact that the individuals within a single colony develop varying body forms, each form specialized for the job it is to do. These different forms are called castes. The fertile males and females carry out the reproductive duties of the colony. The workers, usually sterile individuals, making up the largest percentage of the group, do its basic work. The workers may be further subdivided into a variety of subcastes, each fitted for a particular job. Among the ants certain large, specialized workers are known as soldiers. The termites have a separate soldier caste, also sterile.

Some insects are simply gregarious, gathering in large groups, but this situation is not to be confused with either a subsocial or a social way of life. Gregarious insects may be found in groups for a variety of reasons. They may all be taking advantage of a good food source or may all have hatched in this particular location because of the placement of the eggs from which they developed. Some gregarious insects derive mutual protection by remaining in large groups. Numbers of individuals may take advantage of a particular location in which to hibernate, and some insects migrate in large aggregations. In these gregarious groups, which are simply gatherings of individuals, there is no organization along family lines and no division of labor develops.

In an approach to any subject there must be preliminaries, and having briefly surveyed what we mean by the "social" part of social insects, let us now move to the preliminaries for the "insect" portion of that term. The first step is to fit the insects into the general framework of living things. The animals of the world have been divided into groups, the members of each group showing certain structural similarities. The largest of these groups are called phyla, and all animals placed within a phylum display a certain degree of similarity. Insects belong to the phylum Arthropoda, to which also belong spiders, mites, centipedes, crabs, and many other animals. Animals within each phylum are further subdivided into classes on the basis of structure. Insects have a class all their own called Insecta. Classes are further subdivided into orders. The ants, bees, and wasps all belong to the order Hymenoptera; the termites are the sole members of a separate order, the Isoptera. Each order is subdivided into families, each family into genera, and, finally, each genus is subdivided into species. Each species is a distinct kind of animal. The members of a species are different in one or more ways from all other forms of life. Members of a species are capable of interbreeding and producing fertile offspring. In writing of a single species we use its generic name, which is capitalized, followed by its species name, which is never capitalized. To avoid international confusion, these scientific names are in Latin or in words which have been Latinized, the same name being used world-wide by scientists of all nationalities and languages. Generic and species names are usually printed in italics; the names of phyla, classes, orders, and families in roman type. This practice is followed here.

Man and the social insects share the earth, but the world of one is radically different from the world of the other. In comparing man and insect, the size differences are extreme, the sensory equipment is greatly different, and the means of reacting to stimuli received through the senses are only vaguely similar. The insect lives within the boundaries of its interpretation of the world, and into this insect world man can catch only brief glimpses.

In the two orders containing social insects, Isoptera and Hymenoptera, we find that the insect body is composed of three main parts, the head, thorax, and abdomen. Attached to the head are two long appendages called the antennae. To the thorax are attached six legs, and in some forms two pairs of wings. Insects are turned wrong side-out—they wear their skeletons on the outside of their bodies. They are enclosed within a hard body covering called an exoskeleton, an important ingredient of which is a chemical compound known as chitin. This outer armor is complete with joints to allow for movement. It is textured with furrows, ridges, bumps, and spines. The muscles within the body are attached to the exoskeleton and to various inwardly projecting ridges of the exoskeleton.

The digestive system is basically a tube extending from the mouth to the anus; it is divided into three main sections—the foregut, midgut, and hindgut. In the foregut are the crop and proventriculus, which, as we shall see, assume great importance in some of the social insects. The circulatory system consists of a simple tubular heart that pumps colorless blood out into the body cavities; in most insects there are no blood vessels. The respiratory system consists of air tubes or tracheae that open to the outside through pores called spiracles located along the lower sides of the insect's body. The tracheae ramify throughout the body. The nervous system consists of a brain located in the head, and a nerve cord with ganglia that extends ventrally, that is, on the under side of the body.

These insects typically have compound eyes. Insect eye structure is unlike man's, the insects' compound eyes being composed of a very few to several thousand units called ommatidia. Each ommatidium registers the intensity of the light it receives and the picture perceived by the insect's brain is that of a mosaic of light intensities. Insects do not receive so clear an image as do vertebrates, but their eyes are very sensitive to motion and this is important to them. Some insects also have three simple eyes or ocelli on top of the head. The function of these is not completely understood; they may serve as supplementary light-perception organs. Not all insects have ocelli; not all have compound eyes. Among the ants and termites many species have castes that are completely or very nearly blind.

The sense of taste is located in the mouthparts, but bees, ants, and wasps also have some taste organs on the antennae, and bees can taste to a certain extent with their legs. The sense of smell is located in the insects' jointed antennae. The antennae are also very important organs of touch. The bodies of the insects, despite their hard covering, are well provided with organs receptive to touch. These may be tactile spines and hairs, or sensory cells within the outer covering of the body. Knowledge regarding the reception of sound by insects is limited, and this field is being studied. We shall note auditory reception by the social insects from time to time as we discuss them individually.

Since insects are prisoners in armor, the young, in order to grow, must occasionally shed their old skin and replace it with a larger one secreted by cells beneath the old layer. This process is called molting. Insects undergo varying numbers of molts to reach the adult stage, after which, except in certain rare cases, they no longer grow larger. As they pass through the molts they change in form. This change is known as metamorphosis, and there are two types. In one, complete metamorphosis, the young develops from egg into larva, in which the insect has a body form greatly different from that of the adult; then into pupa, which seems to be a resting stage; and then into the adult. The most familiar example of complete metamorphosis is the butterfly, in which the young develop from egg, to caterpillar, to pupa, to adult butterfly. Among the social insects, wasps, bees, and ants undergo complete metamorphosis. The second type of metamorphosis is known as incomplete or simple metamorphosis; the stages are egg, nymph, and adult. In this type the nymph is very similar in body form to the adult; the main difference is in size. Termites undergo incomplete metamorphosis.

The world of the social insects is one where the inhabitants are very small; where taste, smell, touch, and sometimes—but not always—sight bring messages from the environment; where travel and transportation are either by foot or by wing; where a baby may be a fat, white, wormlike grub one day and a six-legged, winged adult not many days later; where reproduction is the prerogative of a few, and work is the duty of the sterile masses.

Part One

THE WASPS

CHAPTER 1

Hornets

To be "mad as a hornet" is considered to be angry indeed, and to "stir up a hornet's nest" is without doubt to cause a real fuss. Man has a healthy respect for hornets—indeed for all of the wasp group and their well-known stings. Hornets are one kind of wasp; all hornets are wasps, but there are other kinds of wasps in addition to hornets.

The hornets of the genus *Dolichovespula* stand at or near the apex of wasp development, living in colonies of several thousand individuals within walled paper cities of their own construction. In temperate climates a *Dolichovespula* colony is born in the spring, when a queen that has been fertilized the previous fall and has hibernated over the winter months begins the construction of a paper comb in which she lays her first eggs.

This comb starts as a short paper stem, or pedicel, hanging from a support, such as a tree limb. At the bottom of this stem the outline of the first cell of the nest is begun. This cell will ultimately be hexagonal in shape and closely resemble the cell of a honeybee's comb, although the hornet builds with a paper that she manufactures from bits of wood and her saliva, while the honeybee molds her cells from wax produced by her body. Also, whereas the cells of the honeybees' comb lie horizontally, the hornets' cells, like most social wasps' cells, are usually vertical and open downward. The hornet queen starts a second cell on the side of the first. Eventually a third one is formed in the angle made by the first two, and more cells are started in a similar manner until a shelf of cells hanging from the center suspensorium, or support, is formed.

Around these cells the queen also constructs one or more paper walls, which gradually envelop the cells completely, protecting them and their occupants. The paper envelopes are attached to the suspensorium, balloon out about the cells, and draw together, leaving only a small opening at the bottom for the coming and going of the queen. The queen may construct from one to three or possibly four envelopes about the cells, and each of these envelopes is separate from all the others, with a small air space separating each layer.

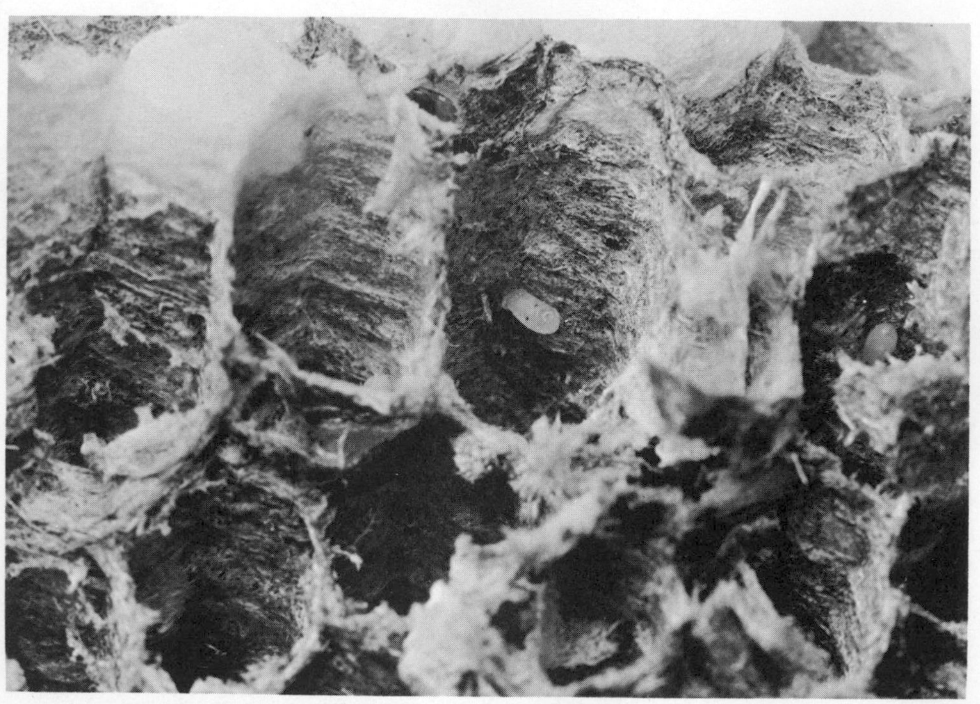

An embryonated wasp egg projects into its paper cell in this view down into the cell. The egg has been attached to the side of the cell, development has started, and soon the larval stage will be begun. The larva will eat and grow until its body fills the cell.

Acting with a seeming inner urgency the hornet queen begins her egg laying even before the first cells have been built to their full length. In each beginning cell she lays a single milky-white egg, which is glued in place at its posterior end. Eventually, the outer covering of the egg slips

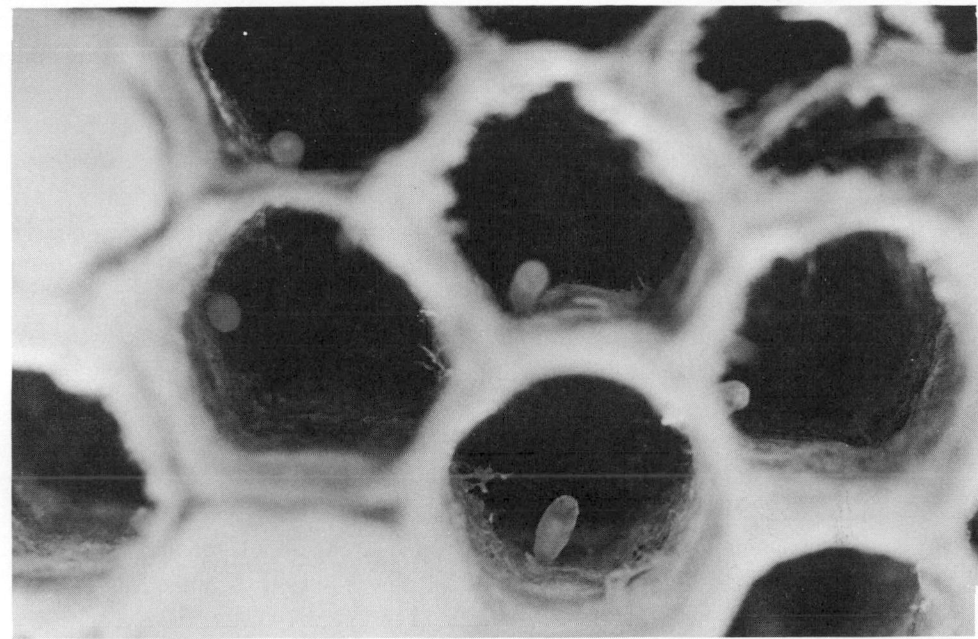

Five embryonated wasp eggs are visible in this view directly into the cells of a wasp nest. This is the beginning stage of development of the wasp egg. Larvae will develop from these eggs, eventually the larvae will become pupae, and finally the adult wasps will emerge to take part in the colony.

down over the emerging larva—the young hornet. These babies, however, bear not the slightest resemblance to their winged, big-eyed, colorful mother, for hornets, as all wasps, undergo a complete metamorphosis in their life history. The larva emerging from the egg is a white, wormish, grublike creature whose only interest in life, apparently, is to eat and thereby to grow.

The burden of satisfying the appetites of the young falls on the founding queen. According to human standards the hornets, as the wasps in general do, have their menus reversed, for in the hornet world it is the young that concentrate on a hearty meat diet, while the adults sip liquids only. The hornet queen, with hungry young to feed, goes hunting for insect prey. When she locates a potential insect dinner, she pounces on it, killing and crushing it with her mandibles. She may carry her booty back to her nest, or she may carve off a portion of it and return later to retrieve the remainder. The prey is chewed by the queen until it is a pasty mass. From this the queen takes much of its liquid content. Some of this liquid provides a part of her own food, but to a greater extent, the hornet queen, like all adult wasps, uses nectar, honeydew, plant sap, or other such sweet juices as the main items in her diet. Very young larvae are fed on part of the liquid from the chewed meat, but as the larvae become slightly older the pellets of meat become their main food item. Sweet juices are an energy food and so are suitable for the adult hornets, but the larvae are growing and require protein for their growth; this the meat provides for them. The queen feeds only the first brood. Later young will be fed these materials by the workers of the colony. As these first young eat and grow, the queen continues her house building, extending the sides of each individual cell to keep pace with the larva's lengthening growth.

The hornet world—and most of the social-wasp world—is upside down. Consider that the hornet young spends its time standing on its head, or rather hanging by its other end. These are strange babies that rest in paper cradles and, it would appear, are in imminent danger of falling out of bed. During their early days they are held in place by a mucus secretion. Later the pressure of the bulk of their bodies against the walls of the cell keeps them from falling.

Each larva eventually finishes its growth and begins to spin a cocoon in which to spend the pupal stage of its life. This cocoon or covering is composed of silk, which is produced by glands in the head of the larva. A part of this cocoon forms a cap over the opening of the cell, neatly sealing the hornet young within its bed. The cocoon covering may completely enshroud the young, or it may taper off toward the posterior section of the insect and not be complete at the bottom.

It is an amazing bit of housekeeping that although the larva's primary activity is eating, during this entire stage no waste products are voided to foul its bed. In the mature larva the collected wastes may be seen as a dark area in the abdomen, showing through the light skin. As the larva prepares to enter the pupal stage, these wastes are voided all at one time. This waste is called the meconium and it becomes a dried pellet in the bottom of the cell.

Within its silken shroud the hornet enters its pupal stage. This appears to be nothing but a resting stage, but actually extreme changes are taking place. Larval tissue is being broken down and remodeled into adult features. In approximately two weeks or less the larva is transformed into the adult hornet. The young adult cuts its way out of the cocoon, and miraculously the wormlike, cell-bound baby has become a winged, mobile member of hornet society.

All of these first young of the queen are destined to be workers in the hornet colony. That is, they are smaller than their mother, are all females, but are sexually immature and do not mate. They take over the duties of the colony, except for egg laying, which they leave to the queen. Workers may occasionally lay eggs—for example, if the queen dies—but as the workers have never mated, these eggs are unfertilized and they develop into males only. On the workers now falls the duty of feeding the queen, her larval young, and themselves. These workers leave the nest, find a source of sweet substances, fill their crops with the juice, and return to the nest where they regurgitate a portion of the liquid, feeding it, mouth to mouth, to other workers or to the queen. Animal juices are also used

Certain solitary wasps known as mud daubers construct cells of mud in which their young develop. Here, removed from their adobe covering, are mud-dauber young. On the left is a cocoon; in the center is a young wasp which is just entering the pupal stage and has been removed by the photographer from the cocoon; and on the right is a pupa in an advanced stage of development, also removed from the cocoon.

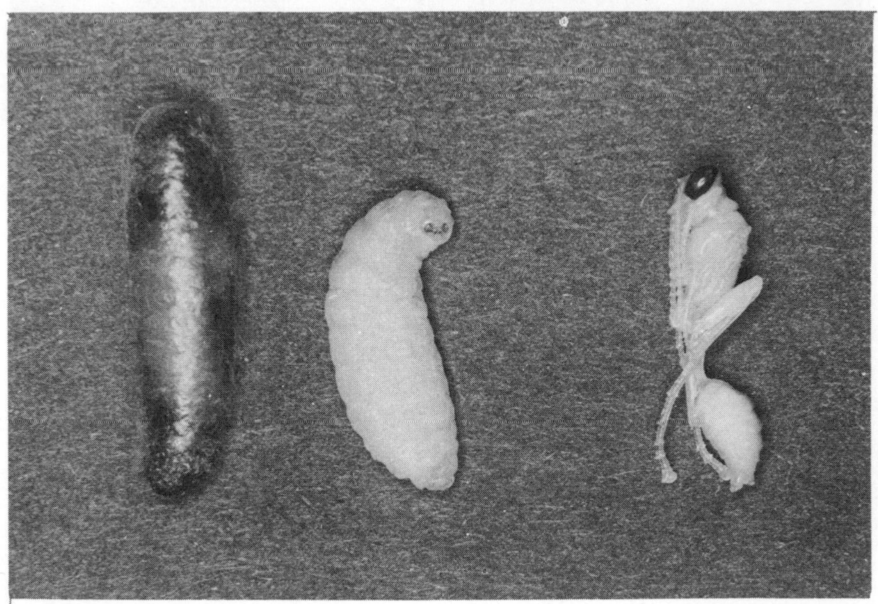

in this way, having been obtained while chewing prey, preparatory to feeding the chewed meat to the larvae. There is thus an exchange of food between adult hornets and a constant feeding of the larvae by the workers. In addition, the larvae, when stimulated by being fed, produce drops of liquid from their mouths. This liquid no doubt serves to lubricate and digest the insect food, but it is also a substance prized by the workers and is eagerly eaten by the adult hornets feeding the larvae. This practice of mutual feeding among members of a colony is known as trophallaxis.

While wasps undergo their pupal transformation, they are completely enclosed within the cell. By removing the upper covering of the cell, the photographer has exposed a young wasp just completing its pupal stage and nearly ready to emerge as an adult.

A rather rough division of labor develops among the workers within the hornet colony. Older workers tend to be the ones who go afield and return with food for the stay-at-homes, and they also bring in wood pulp for the expansion of the nest. The younger workers carry on household duties, distributing the food and using the delivered building materials for work on the nest. They also guard the nest.

With the queen now free from household duties and able to concentrate her resources on producing eggs, and with an ever-increasing crop of workers to expand the home and to feed their growing younger sisters and their mother, the hornet colony begins to grow rapidly. Soon the characteristic oval paper-shrouded hornets' nest begins to take shape.

Did man learn from the hornets and certain other paper-making wasps how to make paper? It is an interesting possibility. Certainly all the time man was laboriously chipping pictures and symbols in rocks by hitting them with other rocks, the wasps were quietly and busily manufacturing their durable paper and forming it into their homes. In fact, certain of the wasps had perfected their own paper-processing technique long before man's appearance on earth. Wasps gather wood fibers from various sources for preparing the paper. These include rotten wood, weather-worn wood, fibers from dead annual plants, fibers from living shrubs, and fibers from man-made paper such as newspapers and cardboard boxes. However, no one species collects from all of these, but rather each species exhibits preferences for certain materials.

The hornet, in gathering the wood fibers, places herself in a position parallel to the grain of the fiber. She then walks backward, tearing off strips of the fiber with her jaws, or mandibles. These wood pieces are held in back of the mandibles until a sufficient quantity has been collected. They are then chewed by the mouthparts, and saliva is added until the wasp has produced a gummy mass.

Returning to the nest, the hornet, or another to whom she may have delivered the building material, adds the paper contribution to the cells being built or to the envelopes surrounding the nest. The hornet holds the ball of pulp along the edge of the already existing paper to which new paper is to be added. By biting into a part of the pulp and through the existing paper, she begins the process of attaching the pulp. Walking backward, she works the pulp into a slender string which she attaches by biting it to the old paper. Walking over the strip repeatedly, she continues to bite the new paper into place and also finally to flatten it out into a strip, which for some species has been reported as measuring something less than ¼ inch in width and from ¾ inch to 1¼ inches in length. Attached and flattened, the addition dries in place.

Like human females, female hornets carry on much rearranging and rebuilding of their nests. They are rather constantly tearing away old envelopes and building new ones in a slightly different place in order to provide room for expansion within the nest. Sometimes cells that have been used numerous times and are no longer useful are also torn away. The paper of which these portions of the nest were composed is then chewed into a pulp once more and used in the rebuilding of the nest. This doubly chewed or sometimes even triply chewed paper appears to be stronger than the original product. In fact, wasp paper varies greatly in strength, depending on the species preparing it, the use to which it is to be put, the number of times it has been reworked, and other factors. The color of the wasp paper varies also, depending on the source of wood fiber being used. Tan, yellow, gray, brown, and white are found, and in some cases several colors are incorporated into one nest.

A great deal of splinter-gathering, saliva-secreting, and chewing on the part of the founding queen must go into her amazing construction of the beginning nest. Eventually her numerous worker daughters take over this job, and by strength of numbers the work progresses rapidly. They add new cells around the periphery of the existing cells until a comb of cells is built which may gradually assume somewhat of an inverted saucer shape. The workers will also begin construction of new paper envelopes and remodeling and expansion of the old envelopes. Eventually a new row of cells will be constructed below the first row. A suspensorium will be built down from the original shelf of cells, or comb, and in line with the original suspensorium of the nest. Building out from the tip of this support, the hornet workers will then construct the second row, or comb, of cells. Later a third, fourth, and additional combs may be added below the earlier ones. In addition to the main suspensorium which suspends one comb from another in the nest, additional bracing suspensoria are also built as the nest expands and the total weight increases.

The additions to the cell structure of the nest require constant razing and rebuilding of the envelopes to provide expansion space and also to provide a constant covering and thereby protection for the contents of the nest. Studies have shown that a large nest of the hornet *Dolichovespula arenaria* will often have 9 to 17 envelopes wrapped about it, and by the time one of these nests has reached 12 inches in diameter 48 to 55 layers will have been built around it, though 35 to 40 of these will have been torn down in the constant "urban-renewal" program. These envelopes with their interspersed air pockets form excellent insulation for the hornets' nest, helping to maintain a more constant temperature within the nest and to prevent overheating. If the interior temperature does become too warm, workers, using their wings, will fan air through the passage from the outside, and some species will bring drops of water into the nest. Evaporation of this water, aided by air movement, provides effective cooling.

Hornets reuse the cells of their nest for brood rearing several times. The queen inserts the tip of her abdomen into cells from which young hornets have recently emerged and lays an egg, thereby restarting the cycle in that cell. Eventually the nest reaches a large size and its length also becomes considerably greater, so that the earlier cells are some distance from the entrance and therefore not convenient to the workers. By this time, too, the earlier cells have already been used several times and are beginning to show signs of wear, in addition to having had the larval meconium deposited in them with each succeeding occupant. The earlier cells are therefore finally abandoned; in some cases they may be partially cut away and the paper reused, or they may be completely walled off with paper.

When the hornet colony has reached a mature size and the end of the summer season—in temperate climates the end of the colony—approaches, special large cells are built. In these are raised new queens. Males are also raised at this time. Males may develop in some of these large-sized cells or in the regular worker-sized cells—both situations are common. The workers may prepare entire combs of large queen cells in the lower portions of the nest; they may also attach queen cells to the periphery of existing combs. Oftentimes both these procedures are followed in one nest. The production of fertile males and females marks the climax of the colony. Upon reaching maturity the virgin queens and the males fly away from the nest, find partners, and mate. Each of these young queens has within her abdomen a sac called the spermatheca in which the supply of sperm she receives from the male is stored. Here the sperm remains viable until needed to fertilize her eggs. In temperate regions, only these fertilized females are destined to survive the approaching winter. They go into hibernation in protected situations and emerge the following spring.

The founding queen of the colony, the mother of these new queens, is literally worn out by her early activity in nest building and the prodigious egg production that followed, and she dies at about this time. Left within the nest may be some males who are hangers-on and some aging workers. In the absence of the queen these workers may make attempts at egg laying. Their efforts are clumsy, however, and they often botch the job by laying more than one egg in a cell. These females produce eggs from which males only develop, and so their efforts do little or nothing to aid the welfare of the colony.

Sometimes a seeming madness comes over these last survivors of the colony and they fail to care for the larvae that remain; they may take them out of the nest and drop them; at times even use them as food. When cold weather arrives the last of the once-prosperous colony dies, with only the hibernating queens surviving to carry the species through to the following year.

The really strange thing is not that the colony falls apart at the end of the season but that such a social organization ever exists at all. These are insects—tiny creatures with at most a very small brain, yet they successfully live in colonies numbering in the thousands, manufacture a building material, construct living quarters for the group, achieve a division of labor, and work for the common welfare.

CHAPTER 2

Yellow Jackets and Other Social Wasps

Yellow jacket is a common name often used for wasps whose way of life is similar to that of the aerial hornets we have been discussing, except for the fact that the yellow jackets typically nest underground. The yellow-jacket queen of the genus *Vespula* establishes her nest in a suitable cavity, such as a rodent burrow, probably hanging the pedicel and the beginning comb from a root or rock projecting into the cavity. The beginning nest bears a close resemblance to that of the hornets, and the queen yellow jacket, like her hornet counterpart, begins construction of a paper envelope about the comb.

As the yellow-jacket family grows it often becomes necessary for the underground cavity to be enlarged. If the soil is hard the workers bring water and regurgitate it onto the dirt walls. Bits of the surrounding walls are then scraped off with the mandibles. The soil may be used for filling openings off the cavity, or pellets of mud may be carried in the mouth and taken outside and dropped. Slowly the chamber is enlarged. When a pebble is encountered it too is taken away, if possible, and dropped. Heavier items may be pushed to the entrance and discarded outside. If the obstacle is large the nest will be built around it.

As with the hornets, the workers construct additional combs below the initial comb, which was begun by the queen and later enlarged by workers. The method used by yellow jackets in adding envelopes differs in some respects from the hornets' pattern, and the former add some lateral supports from the nest wall to the walls of the cavity. On the whole, however, the nests built by hornets and yellow jackets are rather similar, the main difference being in their locations. Living underground gives the yellow jackets a measure of concealment and protection. Whereas the hornets' nests are built where winds and other environmental factors may endanger them, the yellow jackets appear to have rather snug, safe quarters. Probably as a consequence of this, the paper composing the envelopes about the yellow-jacket nests is lighter and less durable than that produced by the hornets.

Near the end of the summer these yellow-jacket nests may reach a large size, more than a foot in diameter, and over the life of the colony may have housed 25,000 individuals, although probably no more than 5000 would be alive at any one time.

All social wasps belong to the family Vespidae in the order Hymenoptera. Within the family Vespidae are various subfamilies containing the social wasps. One of these is the subfamily Vespinae to which belong the hornets (we discussed the genus *Dolichovespula* as an example) and the yellow jackets (we discussed the genus *Vespula*). Another genus within this subfamily is *Vespa,* of which the only representative in the United States is *Vespa crabro,* or the so-called European hornet, which was introduced here and now occurs in the eastern part of the country. *Vespa crabro* is found nesting in a variety of places—in exposed situations, underground, in buildings, and in hollow trees. Occasionally with this species the outer paper envelope is not used or is much reduced, as when a nest is located in a well-protected situation. The life history of this wasp is similar to that described for the hornets and yellow jackets.

A second subfamily of social wasps is Polistinae. This subfamily includes the *Polistes* wasps, which we shall discuss shortly, and also a group known as the polybiine wasps. In the past this latter group was accorded separate subfamily status, but certain authorities have recently placed it within the subfamily Polistinae.

The polybiine wasps are most widely represented in the tropical areas of South America and Central America but are also found in smaller numbers in Asia and Africa. Living in the tropics, these wasps need never adjust to the coming of winter. Whereas the hornets and yellow jackets, when living in temperate areas, produce colonies that are annual affairs and must come to an end in the fall, with only the young queens having the bodily reserves to live through the winter, the tropical polybiine colonies are ongoing affairs. Consequently new polybiine colonies are founded by one or more young fertilized queens, who leave the established nest, taking with them a group of the workers. This nucleus then establishes a new colony and in this way avoids many of the dangers faced in the temperate regions by a solitary queen attempting to found a colony alone. Unlike most of the wasps of cooler regions, these tropical wasp colonies often have multiple queens, a circumstance which enables the colony to grow rapidly and maintain a large population.

The polybiine group of wasps is a large one with many diverse species, ranging from those that build only small combs without a protective envelope and never attain a large population, to those that build large enclosed nests similar to the hornets' nests of temperate regions. The architectural style of some of these larger nests, however, varies from the hornets' nests in some interesting ways. Like the hornets' nests these particular polybiine nests are often hung from branches and consist at first of a single comb hung from the support, the individual cells opening downward. A paper envelope is built about the comb with an opening in the envelope at the bottom center to allow for the going and coming of the

Half the paper envelope was cut away from this polybiine wasp nest to expose in a longitudinal section its interior arrangement. The nest, hung from an acacia tree in southern Mexico, was approximately six inches in length. Entrance to the interior was through the opening at the bottom.

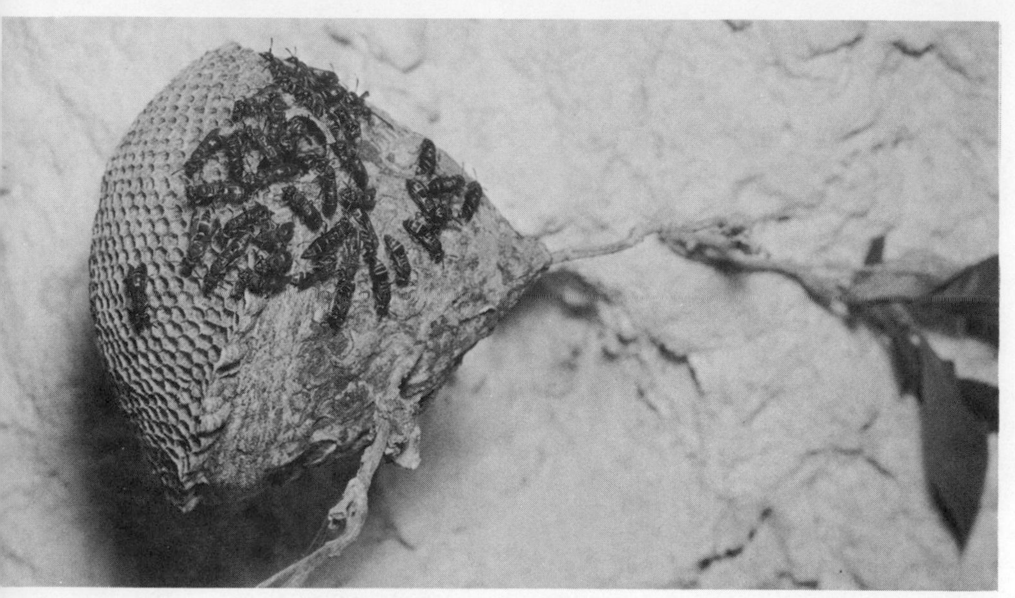

This tropical American polybiine wasp nest was photographed near Vera Cruz, Mexico. Within the paper covering are several combs. A new comb is under construction on the outside of the paper envelope. Eventually the envelope will be built down and around this new comb also. The wasps are clustered about the entrance to the interior.

An abandoned polybiine wasp nest with a portion of the outer envelope removed shows the arrangement of combs within the nest. Each comb is attached to the paper envelope at its periphery.

wasps. Unlike the hornets and yellow jackets, however, the polybiine wasps build the envelope flush with the edges of the comb. When a second comb is built, the cells are started on the outside of the bottom of the envelope, being built out in the open, rather than inside the envelope. The central entrance hole is allowed to remain in the center of the new comb. Eventually the envelope is extended down and about the new comb, finally enclosing it within the nest. A third comb and later ones will be built in the same manner, so that eventually the nest becomes a long cylinder, with each comb built flush against the inside portion of the covering envelope and access to all tiers of combs being only through the center hole in each comb.

One of the most interesting of the polybiine wasps is *Brachygastra (Nectarina) lecheguana,* the honey wasp. The New World tropics are the established home of this wasp, but it extends south to Brazil and north to the southernmost tip of Texas at Brownsville. This wasp stores honey in its nest, as do the honeybees. All adult wasps live primarily on sweet plant juices, and they do carry quantities of this liquid back to their nest with them, regurgitating it to nest mates. The honey wasp has carried this practice to its logical conclusion and developed the habit of storing these juices in empty cells within the nest. The nectar is evidently concentrated in some manner to form a thick honey which will remain in the cells, for they are reported as generally opening downward in the usual wasp fashion and as not being capped. Some species of *Polistes* wasps, which we will discuss shortly, also store a very small amount of honey in their nests.

So little is actually known about these honey wasps that no one is quite positive as to how the honey is used. It is generally assumed that the honey may well be stored to help the adult wasps through unfavorable periods, such as drought, when food is not normally available. Some scientists believe that the honey, supplemented with pollen, may be fed to the larvae, although others believe that the honey is used by the adult wasps only and the larvae are fed at least primarily on meat, as is the case with most wasps. However, one subfamily of solitary wasps, the Masarinae, is known to mass-provision the individual tubular cells in which the young develop with a food supply of pollen and nectar, and so use of honey and pollen as a diet for the larvae may be a possibility for the honey wasps. One use for this honey is known, however. That is by man. In these New World tropics where sweets were formerly, and sometimes still are, not easy to obtain, the native people cut down mature nests of honey wasps and drain out the honey for their own use.

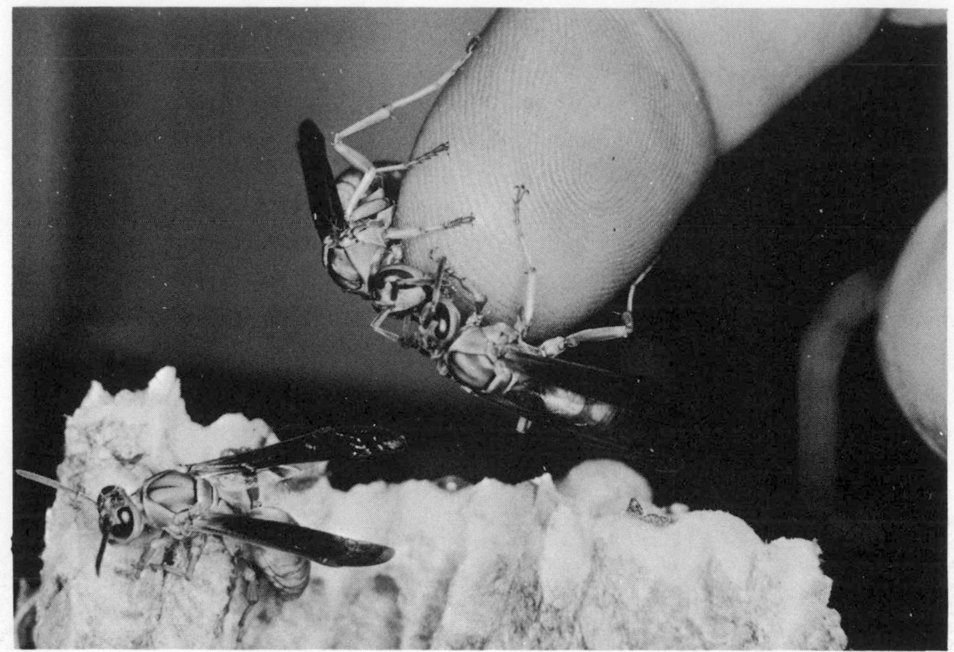

Honey served on the end of a human finger to these captive wasps was just as acceptable to them as honey served elsewhere. They readily ate it whenever it was offered and made no attempt to sting the hand that fed them.

New colonies of these honey wasps are started by swarms which may include several queens. They build a typical large aerial nest of several combs, each attached to the nest wall, which is composed of a single layer of paper. Strangely this species also may build combs on the sides, rather than on the bottom of the nest wall, thus forming some combs that open horizontally, in addition to the combs in the usual position. These colonies are perennial, with multiple queens to populate them and no frost to slow their development. Therefore, the nests reach a large size, up to 20 inches in length, and the wasp population is reported to reach as high as 15,000.

The wasps most familiar to the majority of people living in temperate zones are those of the genus *Polistes,* mentioned as also being members of the subfamily of wasps known as the Polistinae. The *Polistes* wasps build small exposed combs, often located in such man-made environs as under eaves, on porches, and in sheds and barns. In addition to building nests in man's immediate habitat, the hibernating queens often choose to do their

This beginning nest of Polistes flavus *hangs suspended from an upper support. The cells open downward, and larvae can be seen in some of them. These cells are left exposed, not covered by a protective envelope as is the case with some wasps.*

winter resting inside his houses, thereby sometimes causing consternation to the housewife who finds them buzzing and reconnoitering on warm days when spring approaches.

The generic name *Polistes* is from the Greek and means "founder of a city." While the *Polistes* do found wasp cities, they are mere country cousins compared to their relatives the hornets and yellow jackets, who found colonies with larger populations and much fancier walled paper cities in which to house themselves.

The life history of a *Polistes* colony is similar to that of the hornets and yellow jackets. The fertilized queen, who has hibernated through the winter, begins her nest by constructing a paper pedicel hung on high from a somewhat sheltered location. At the tip of the pedicel the cells take shape and so the comb begins and grows as does that of the hornets. However, the *Polistes* nest in the temperate zones never grows beyond the one comb, and this is never covered by protecting envelopes. Nevertheless, variations in nest building do occur among *Polistes*. Some tropical species may build the comb off-center from the point of attachment so that it has a slanting appearance and the cells open to the side, rather than downward.

The first adult wasps that emerge from the cells of the *Polistes* nest are quite similar in size and appearance to the queen, as will also be the later young produced in the colony. This is in contrast to the queens and their daughter workers in the hornet and yellow-jacket nests, where more differences between the two castes are often apparent. The *Polistes* daughters produced by the founding queen take over the role of workers, and the *Polistes* city grows, completing its cycle before the coming of winter. Relationships between the female wasps in a *Polistes* colony are less clear-cut than in the more highly socially evolved and larger colonies of hornets and yellow jackets, and the *Polistes* queen's position is sometimes less secure and more open to usurpation by other females in the nest than is the case among the hornets and yellow jackets.

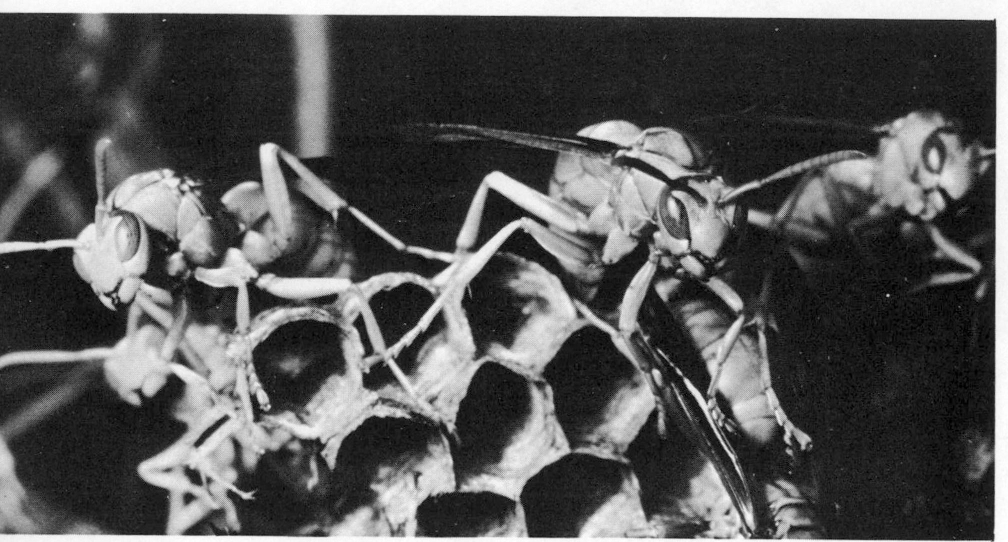

These big-eyed, yellow-bodied Polistes *wasps stand guard on their nest, which consists of a single comb hanging exposed in a shrub. The photograph, taken in the late fall, shows the cells to be empty, with no more young being raised. These wasps are formidable and readily came to the defense of the nest when it was approached.*

One species, *Polistes annularis,* found in North America, at times has colonies founded by a single queen, as is considered to be typical for most temperate-zone *Polistes,* but sometimes this same species has colonies founded cooperatively by several queens. The original founder may be joined by a second queen, and the two then work together. They may later be joined by others. Some of these females may have already started their own combs and yet will abandon these beginnings—even including larvae—to join in establishing a multi-queen nest.

A similar situation occurs in a European species, *Polistes gallicus,* which has received a great deal of study. In northerly climates, colonies of this species were found to have been established by single queens. In warmer climates to the south, however, the tendency was for colonies to be established by multiple queens as has been noted for *P. annularis.* An interesting situation develops in these temperate-zone colonies where several queens establish a nest. Before long one of these queens begins to assume a dominant position over the others. She tends to do more and more of the egg laying. The subordinate females begin to lay eggs less and to work more, becoming increasingly workerlike in their duties. Eventually the dominant one becomes the "queen" of the nest and the others carry out the mundane household activities. These fit into the role of workers, even though they are fertilized females, which the regular workers, when they appear, are not.

Exactly how the dominance of the queen over these other fertilized females is achieved is not completely understood, but it is known that in some cases the queen destroys eggs laid by the subordinate females; she may take the initiative and keep the cells filled with eggs to prevent the others from laying in them; and there is probably a psychological factor involved, wherein a subordinate position in the social hierarchy has a physiological effect on the wasp that causes a failure to lay eggs.

Some experiments on *P. gallicus* led to the conclusion that a scale of dominance exists among these females which is similar to the "peck order" among chickens. The dominant queen in such a group was found to have well-developed ovaries, the female in rank directly below her to have slightly smaller ovaries, the one below her to have ovaries smaller yet, and so on down through the group. If the dominant queen is removed from the nest, the queen holding the "rank" next below her usually assumes the dominant position. The dominant female probably demands and receives more of the food than her lesser nest mates and this may be a factor in her development of larger ovaries. Conversely, less food may cause a reduction in size of the ovaries of the subordinate females. Perhaps merely use or non-use of the ovaries may also have an effect on their size.

But exactly how does the dominant queen assume that position? We really have not yet answered that basic question. We can say, as suggested earlier, that perhaps the dominance is a psychological condition that has physiological effects—but with what attributes is one female more endowed to enable her to achieve a psychological dominance? And exactly how does the psychological affect the physiological? These are questions that we cannot always answer well on a human level either.

Going back to that versatile wasp, *P. gallicus,* which starts single-queen nests in northern Europe, and establishes multi-queen nests in which one queen becomes dominant farther south in Europe, we find that when it was studied in the warmth of the Sahara new colonies were found to be established by the swarming of a queen and a group of workers. This one species, then, has three rather different ways of founding colonies, depending more or less on the climate in which they are located. *Polistes* wasps living in the tropics probably found new colonies by swarming, as does *P. gallicus* in the warmer parts of its range. We have noted that polybiine wasps, largely tropical inhabitants, also found new colonies by swarming.

It is postulated that social wasps originally developed in the tropics. Here young could be produced rather constantly—the weather was favorable

Polistes canadensis navajoe *is shown here drinking from a small water hole in a stream bed in southern Arizona. Many of the wasps, such as this one with her long, filmy wings and large eyes, are particularly attractive insects.*

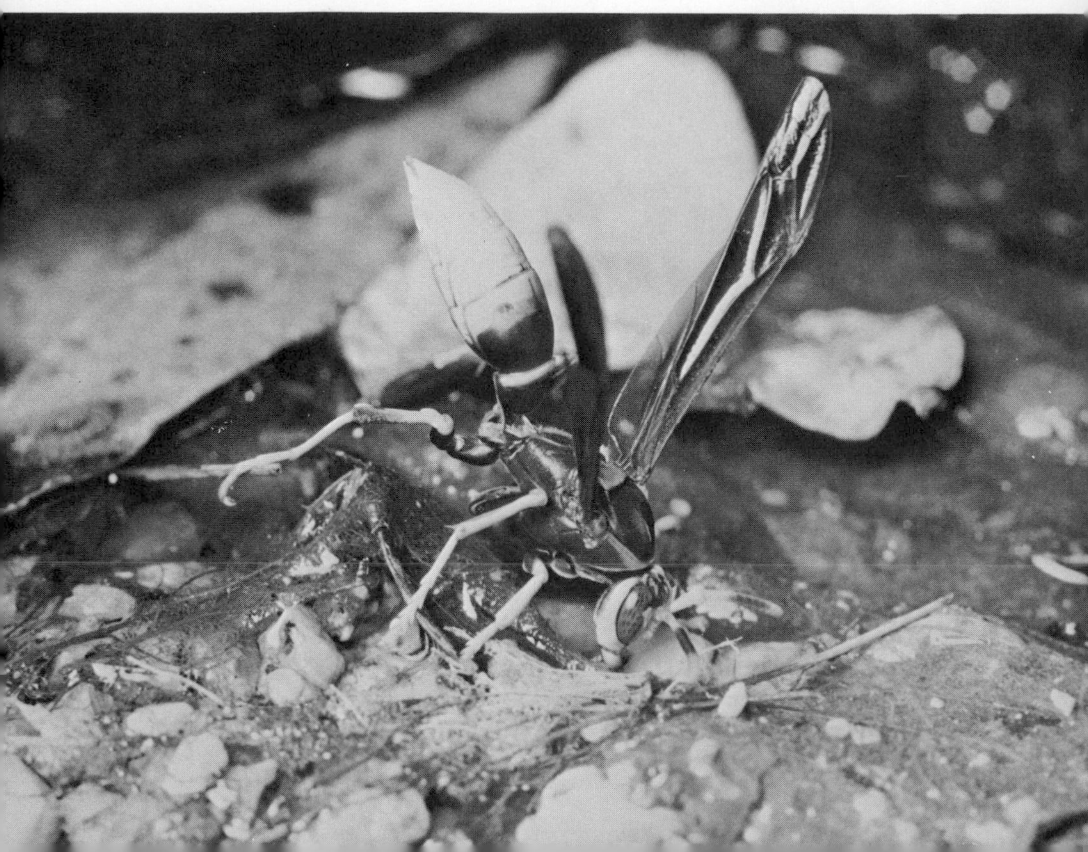

and food supplies were sufficient. Under these conditions the typical social wasp nest was probably one with multiple queens doing the egg laying and new colonies being produced by the swarming of one or several queens with a group of workers. Certain of these wasps were able to invade the temperate areas only as they developed queens endowed with sufficient bodily reserves to hibernate through unfavorable periods when the remainder of the colony was doomed to die. That some were remarkably successful at this is attested by *Polistes,* the hornets, and the yellow jackets.

Why, though, if a queen is produced in late summer, her body in prime condition, and fertilized by a male, does she not attempt to found a colony at once? In the tropics this would appear to be the case, but the temperate-zone queen enters a hibernation or resting state until the following spring. She cannot in all cases be warned by cooler weather, for many queens enter their hibernation early in the fall before cooler weather has arrived. Is there built into her physiologically the need for this pause, or the need for a cooler period, or some other need, before her body is ready to produce eggs and begin building the nest? Such a resting period is necessary in many living things, including seeds. But if social wasps arose in tropical climates where such a pause is supposedly unnecessary, exactly how did this need or condition develop in temperate areas? The study of wasps, like that of most living things, sometimes raises as many questions as it answers.

CHAPTER 3

Solitary and Parasitic Wasps

The vast majority of wasps do not move in social circles. Most of them lead solitary lives. This would seem to be in complete contradiction to all we have been saying. Certainly the hornets, yellow jackets, polybiine wasps, and *Polistes* wasps are anything but solitary in habit, but these types are the elite among the wasps. Almost all of the other wasps are solitary, a few are considered subsocial, and only a very few have reached a real social level.

Actually the term "wasp" covers a lot of territory, it being a name given to a large and diverse number of species within the order Hymenoptera. One large group of these insects, known as the terebrants, or as the parasitic Hymenoptera, includes the ichneumon wasps, the gall wasps, and others. In this group the female has an ovipositor, or egg-laying structure, which is used for laying eggs in insect prey or in some other location typical for the species. The stock from which developed the true wasps many millions of years ago is believed to have belonged to this group. Today, its members, although of the order Hymenoptera, are far removed from the true wasps, and so at this point we leave them. A second group within the Hymenoptera, the Aculeata, includes, in addition to a large group of solitary wasps, the social wasps and also the bees and ants. With the aculeate wasps an important change has taken place—the eggs leave the female's body through the genital aperture, and the ovipositor has become modified into a sting.

While we are mainly interested in the social wasps, a look at certain of their solitary relatives can give us some clues as to how the social wasps may have ascended the evolutionary ladder to their present lofty heights.

Strange and varied are the ways in which living things provide food for their young, and one of the most unusual is the method that has been evolved through the ages by certain solitary wasps. The female solitary wasp finds her specific type of prey, an insect or spider, and stings it. The prey is usually not killed but is paralyzed as a result of the venom injected by the sting. On or near the prey the wasp lays her egg, and the larva that develops from the egg feeds upon the still-living fresh meat which is helpless to resist or escape. Eventually the prey succumbs, but not until the larva has eaten its fill and achieved its growth. Thus, endowed with neither mammary glands nor refrigeration, the female solitary wasps still manage to provide fresh food for their young, although in most cases the mothers will never be in contact with their offspring. Since the sting developed from the ovipositor, the male is stingless and has but one purpose in life—fertilization of the female.

The methods these lone females use in dealing with their paralyzed prey and in preparing a location for their eggs and the prey give an indication of the positions of the different species on the evolutionary scale. Considered to be lowest in rank are those species of solitary wasps in which the female simply finds the larva of some insect, such as that of a beetle in the ground, stings it, lays her egg upon it, and leaves it where it was found, making no effort to provide protection for the wasp larva that will develop upon the food.

Advancement in rank takes place when the wasp, after stinging the prey, drags it into a hole or crevice. After placement of the prey the wasp lays her egg upon it. The young is thus somewhat protected by its location. This stage of development is exemplified by a group of wasps, the Pompilidae, commonly known as spider wasps because they prey specifically on spiders. Among the most spectacular of the spider wasps are the tarantula hawks of the genus *Pepsis*. These are large wasps, some with a body length up to 1½ inches. One species is steel-blue and black with large red wings. These wasps paralyze the very large spiders known as tarantulas. These spiders may have a body 2 inches or more in length, in addition to long legs which give them a greater overall length. The tarantula is a long-lived creature, the females having been known to reach maturity at about 10 years of age, and to live to be 25 years old. A tarantula hawk manages to sting and immobilize a tarantula, drags it to a cavity in the ground, and there lays an egg upon it. The wasp then leaves, having provided food for the young she will never see.

The tarantula hawk is a solitary wasp of impressive size. The female hunts and stings a tarantula, a very large, hairy, black spider. The sting does not kill the tarantula, but immobilizes it. As shown above, the wasp drags the spider to a hole, lays her egg upon it, and the wasp larva gradually consumes the still-living tarantula. Eventually the tarantula dies, but not until it has provided sufficient fresh meat for the wasp to complete its larval stage.

Still higher in the scale are those solitary wasps that first prepare a cell of some type, perhaps in sand, and then find, sting, and bring the prey back to the cell. Some of the most interesting of the solitary wasps that exhibit this way of life are certain species of the genus *Ammophila,* which prepare a cell by digging in the soil. This completed, the female flies about the area, visually learning the location of her nest. Going hunting afield, she locates and paralyzes her prey, typically a caterpillar, drags it back to her nest, deposits it, and lays her egg upon it. The burrow is filled with dirt and then this particular wasp, most amazingly and most unlike any other wasp, picks up a pebble in her mandibles, and with her head bobbing up and down tamps down the earth to fill the cavity. The use of tools by animals is rare indeed, but *Ammophila's* use of a pebble has been verified by observers numerous times. Within the cell in the earth the wasp larva will emerge from the egg, feed upon the caterpillar, enter the pupal stage, and eventually emerge, as an adult, from the cell to the surface above.

The tiny mud houses of some of the solitary wasps are familiar adornments under eaves and in old buildings. Built by the wasps called mud daubers, these are cells in which their young will develop. The female wasp collects tiny balls of mud which she carries to a chosen location. Here she applies the mud pellets, using her mandibles and feet, and builds them into a tubular cell against the wall or other support. This completed, she begins her hunt. Returning to the nest with a paralyzed spider, she places her egg on it and tucks it neatly into the cell. But here something new and more advanced has been added—she paralyzes several more spiders, inters them in the cell, and then finally seals it with more mud, leaving inside the promise of one larva to come, and more than one course for its dinner. This provision of more than one piece of food for the larva is a step toward the feeding habits of social wasps, which bring food daily to their larvae. The female mud dauber may then go on to construct more such cells adjacent to the completed one or may build other cells elsewhere.

Another builder with mud belongs to the genus *Eumenes* and is known as a potter wasp. This creature constructs tiny, delicate clay pots, rounded and full at the base with a narrow neck and flaring lip, reminiscent of a handmade Indian pot. Or perhaps we should acknowledge precedence and say the Indian pots are reminiscent of the cells of the potter wasps. These miniature vases are individual cells in which the young of these wasps will develop. The cells are constructed on branches or twigs by solitary females who transport the mud to the location and mold it instinctively. These cells are stocked with numerous tiny caterpillars, but here yet another advance has taken place. Some species of *Eumenes* lay the egg first, before any prey is obtained. This reminds us of the social wasps' practice of laying each egg in an empty cell. With *Eumenes,* however, when the egg has been placed in the empty cell, prey is added. Some species of this wasp have an arrangement whereby the egg is hung from a filament within the cell, probably to protect the egg from being mashed by its prepared dinner. The jug, once it is fully provisioned, is then sealed with more mud, and the young wasp eats and develops within.

The wasps we have been describing practice what is known as mass provisioning. That is, they stockpile all the food their young will need and then go on about their business, their duties to the young having been discharged. Some solitary wasps, however, have advanced to progressive provisioning. These feed their young over a period of time as they develop. Thus they have established an important contact between mother and young that does not occur with mass provisioning.

Previously we described some species of *Ammophila* that practice mass provisioning. Other species of *Ammophila,* however, are known to practice progressive provisioning and to maintain three nests at one time. These nests consist of individual burrows in the soil. As each is constructed it is stocked with a caterpillar, the wasp egg is laid on the prey, and the nest is closed. When sufficient time has elapsed for the larva to have consumed the caterpillar, the mother wasp returns, opens the burrow, and provides more food. The burrow is usually examined on each day from then, and the necessary care given it during that day. The nests, having been established at varying times, will contain young in differing degrees of development, yet the female wasp is capable of remembering the location of each and of giving to each the care that her daily inspection indicates is needed.

Increasing maternal solicitude is shown by the wasp *Synagris cornuta.* The young of this wasp are not only fed each day by their mother but fed the prey in a macerated form, as are the young of the social wasps.

In Africa lives a wasp genus, *Belonogaster,* in which a female builds a comb much like the simple comb of a *Polistes* queen. This is composed of paper, and the female lays an egg in each cell as it takes shape. The larvae are fed macerated prey, after a time enter the pupal stage, and upon emergence stay for a time with their mother on the nest. These young, however, are all fertile individuals—that is, either males or females that are capable of mating and do eventually mate. There are no infertile workers in the colony. Nevertheless, a rough division of labor does seem to take place, with the younger females often doing household chores, such as feeding the young and later hunting. Evidently the older females do most of the egg laying. The young produce droplets of oral secretion that are imbibed by the workers. This wasp has therefore advanced to a social situation: the founding mother lives long enough so that her life span overlaps that of her children; in addition, the young remain with their mother; there is some division of labor; females care for young that may include their own but also include young that are not theirs; and trophallaxis occurs—the young are fed by the adults, and the salivary secretion produced by the larvae is eaten by the adults.

From *Belonogaster* it is only a short step to the *Polistes* wasps we discussed as examples of social wasps. That step consists of the production by *Polistes* of a first brood (and also of later broods) made up of females that do not mate but seem to be underdeveloped, and this marks the birth

This insect commonly known as a velvet ant is not an ant at all, but rather is a solitary wasp. These mutillid wasps are often brightly colored with red or yellow abdomens. It is the female only which is antlike in appearance, for the male is winged. Mutillids are parasites of certain bees and wasps.

of the worker class among the wasps. Among *Polistes* wasps there is little obvious physical difference between the queen and the workers—they are of much the same size and appearance—but there is a difference in behavior. However, when we advance to the highest level—that of the yellow jackets and hornets—the physical differences between the queen and the workers are obvious, primarily consisting of the larger size of the queen, although in some cases there may also be small differences in color and structure. On this higher level there are also clear-cut behavioral differences between the two forms.

There are literally thousands of species of solitary wasps, representing a wide range of evolutionary advancement. From the solitary wasp who simply lays an egg on the paralyzed food for its young, leaving the lunch and the baby wherever the lunch happens to be, through the intermediate stages of constructing underground, plant-enclosed, or adobe cells for the young, progressive provisioning, and food maceration, and finally to the social wasps living in paper cities of their own construction, with the care of the young undertaken by several adults working cooperatively, the trail is long and involved. Probably the ancestors of the most advanced wasps did not specifically follow every one of these steps in their progress upward, but the solitary-wasp species we see today give us some indications of the possible development of wasp society.

There is one more step, however, on this evolutionary path. In human terms it is a step down, but in wasp terms it is simply another adaptation to conditions presented and as such is fairly successful. A few species of wasps have become parasites and depend completely on their hosts to raise their young for them. So dependent have they become that they no longer have any workers of their own—these parasitic species consist only of fertile females and males. Each of them preys on a specific close relative—for example, *Vespula austriaca* is parasitic on *Vespula rufa,* and parasitic *Polistes* queens prey on related species of *Polistes.* The parasitic queen enters an established nest belonging to one of her relatives and lays her eggs in the cells. Her young are raised, all unsuspecting, by the workers of the colony. Not a great deal is known about what transpires within the nest, but before long, while the developing brood may include a few workers and males of the host species, increasingly the sexual forms of the invading species make up the bulk of the emerging adults. Evidently the original founding queen of the colony dies or is killed soon after the entrance of the usurper. With her dies any chance for future workers. Eventually the colony population in the nest consists of the two sexes of adult wasps of the interloper species, who will eventually leave, mate, and carry on their own family line at the expense of other more industrious relatives.

CHAPTER 4

Organization of Wasp Colonies

What is the value of a social way of life for the wasps? What advantages are derived from it? Certainly with the wasps' social systems there is a more economical and efficient use of energy and resources. That is, the egg-laying activities are centered in one or a few individuals in the colony, leaving all the other females to devote themselves solely to other necessary jobs. The workers' energy is thus not split into two diverse directions. Also the infertile females are "cheaper" to produce than are fertile females or queens. Therefore more workers than queens can be produced at a certain cost. By restricting the egg laying to a few of the more expensive models and by also restricting the production of these models to a brief period, an economical efficiency is achieved. Another economy is the restriction on males. These are produced when they are needed, but their life span is short, and the colony need not support them for any great length of time. Social life also provides increased protection for the young. How much better protected are the young of the hornets, guarded by the workers' stings, than the young of solitary wasps, left on their own to develop.

The end result of these advantages provided by the wasps' social way of living is the efficient production of large numbers of the species, including queens and males for insuring the production of future generations. Since the continuation of the species is the basic purpose of insect activity, the social wasps can be considered as highly successful.

Granted that the social way of life is advantageous, certainly the wasps cannot logically determine this. Why, then, do they live in societies, or, in other words, what binds a group of individuals into a social whole?

No one is ready to answer that question with any certainty, but one factor may be gustatory greed.

Trophallaxis, or mutual feeding among members of a colony, has already been mentioned. Among the wasps this includes the imbibing of a liquid secretion from the larvae's mouths by the adults. This liquid is produced by the labial glands of the larvae; these are the same glands that will eventually produce the silk from which the pupal cocoons will be spun and that will produce a liquid secretion in the adult wasps. A larva emits a drop of this liquid when macerated food is offered to it by a worker, and the liquid is usually quickly eaten by the worker. Apparently the workers are eager to obtain this liquid, for they often tease or trick the larvae into producing the drops by touching or pinching the babies' heads and then give no meat in return. In fact, it is reported that if a larva will not produce for a greedy worker, the worker may seize the larva's head, jerk the young part way out of the cell, and ram it back down into bed. This larval secretion is believed to be sweet and for this reason relished by the workers, queen, and males of the colony. One hypothesis is that this production of a desired substance by the young for the older members of the colony is a motivating factor toward holding these individual insects in a social

Trophallaxis, or the mutual exchange of food, is an important means of colony organization among many social insects. Here two wasps exchange food. Their legs grasp one another, their antennae bring them sensations from their surroundings, and their mouthparts meet in the food exchange.

organization. Another train of scientific thought, however, contends that this labial secretion is not desired by the workers but is simply removed as a hygienic measure to keep the nest clean. Experiments with one species of *Vespula* showed that the larval oral secretion was not relished by adults. In this case, however, there is a possibility that at one time this secretion was important to the workers and that they have since evolved beyond this stage.

That trophallaxis is not always a vital factor in the development of social-insect societies is demonstrated, however, by some social-bee species. These bees have no direct contact with their larvae, which develop in closed cells that contain food mass-provisioned for the young. Obviously even the most basic factors, such as the motivation that actually holds a group of several thousand hornets in a cohesive whole, are far from being completely understood at present.

In temperate climates at least there comes a time when the wasp colony's social organization begins to break down. We noted when discussing the hornets that when the summer season is ending and the crop of males and queens has been produced by the colony, aberrant behavior often becomes apparent among the workers. Larvae may simply die in numbers, or in some species the larvae may be killed and eaten by the workers. Just exactly what causes these actions is not known. It may be that as summer nears its end there is a general lack of food—the adults may lack sufficient food for their needs and may be demanding more salivary secretion than the young, who are also short of food, can produce. The queen exerts a stabilizing influence over a colony—probably both psychologically and physiologically—and by this late period in the development of the colony this influence may be much reduced as a result of her aged and worn-out condition, or may be completely absent if she is already dead. This lessening or absence of the queen's influence may have a bearing on the disintegration of the colony. It is also probable that the workers' bodies—perhaps because of limited food, or lowered environmental temperatures, or other factors—do not produce certain secretions ordinarily fed to the larvae as liquids or incorporated into their dinners of meat by the workers' prechewing of these. Lack of these secretions, or changes in them, may cause the larvae to die or to develop abnormally. As we move on to the other social insects we shall see that secretions passed about the colony by trophallaxis play an important part in colony organization. That the same effects occur among the wasps is a very definite probability.

It was with the birth of the worker class that the wasps entered upon a truly social life. These workers pose another riddle. How did they develop? Why were the females produced by the egg-laying female wasp not simply more females capable of mating and being so-called perfect females themselves? Probably the cause is malnutrition. When the queen of a social wasp species is founding her colony she is an exceedingly busy lady. She feeds her young progressively and must hunt and bring home each day sufficient food to feed her developing brood. Her body is producing eggs. The nest needs additions. The individual cell walls must be lengthened as the larvae grow, for eggs were laid in these cells when their construction was barely started. The queen herself needs food. It would not be surprising if this first brood of young were undernourished, and this malnutrition may result in underdeveloped reproductive systems.

This explanation seems logical in regard to the first brood of young. However, after the first workers have been produced and are available to house-build and hunt for the later young, presumably sufficient food should be available so that these next young would be perfect females, assuming that food is the causative factor. These usually develop into more workers, however. But here again the workers' habit of taking salivary secretion from the larvae may play a part. As we have mentioned, the workers often "milk" the larvae excessively, causing the larvae to give back to the colony almost as many nutrients as they have received. This excessive milking may therefore cause malnutrition also, whereby these young, like the first brood, are prevented from obtaining sufficient food to develop into perfect females.

This leads us to wonder how perfect females or queens can ever be produced. As the size of the colony grows, there is an increasingly larger percentage of workers to larvae. At this later time, then, personnel would be sufficient to provide adequate food supplies for the whole colony. Of course there would also be more workers presumably demanding secretions from the larvae. Perhaps, however, the supply of nectar and other sweets from outside the colony would be this time be so plentiful that fewer demands would be made upon the larvae for their sweet secretion. Therefore plentiful food for the entire colony may be the signal for production of sexual forms.

Among the yellow jackets and hornets special large-sized queen cells are built and in these all the new queens are reared. The size of these cells may signal the workers to feed the larvae in these more abundantly or to feed them a different diet than is fed the workers in normal-sized cells. However, it is only among some of the most highly evolved species that queen cells are constructed. In *Polistes* colonies there are no differentiated cells. And in those species having them, who or what gives a signal to the workers to build larger-than-normal cells?

Secretions may be the catalysts that cause the development of queens. Chemical secretions produced within the bodies of adult wasps, passed on to the larvae through food fed them by the workers, may affect the larvae, determining whether they will become workers or queens. Experiments have shown that when the wasp workers were kept warm both night and day, queens were produced from the larvae for which they were caring. The temperature at which the larvae themselves were kept had no bearing on the final outcome. It may be, therefore, that the temperature affects the workers and the secretions they produce, these secretions, in turn, affecting the larvae they feed.

We have ignored up to this point another important, although short-lived, segment of the colony—the males. These are produced by unfertilized eggs, whereas females, both queens and workers, are produced by fertilized eggs. The queen wasp mates once and in her spermatheca is stored the supply of sperm she receives from the male, which will last for her entire lifetime of egg production. An egg, before it leaves the queen's body, is fertilized by one of the sperm if it is destined to become a female. If a male, fertilization never takes place.

Workers do not mate, but under some circumstances, as in the absence of a queen, they do lay eggs. These are unfertilized and therefore develop into male wasps. Males are primarily produced, however, by unfertilized eggs laid by the queen, and these are not produced randomly throughout the season, but occur in large numbers at approximately the same time as numbers of queens are also developing from the queen's eggs. It is interesting—and further confusing—that in those species which prepare larger queen cells, males may be found developing either in the larger queen-size cells, or in the regular worker-size cells. The development of males and queens signifies the high point of the colony, at least in temperate regions. Conditions pertaining to food and secretions may be the explanation for the production of queens. While we know how males are produced—that is, by unfertilized eggs—we still do not know exactly what triggers the queen to lay unfertilized eggs at this particular time.

Man still knows relatively little about the wasps. We know generally how they live, but actually very little of why they function as they do. The wasps in temperate climates have received the most study, because it is in these areas that the majority of the observers and scientists have lived and worked. Yet although wasps probably developed in the tropics and many interesting species live exclusively in the tropics today, these remain relatively little studied.

To be quite truthful, wasps are not the easiest things in the world to study. It is far easier for an entomologist to devote himself to breeding fruit flies in a jar, counting mosquito larvae per unit of water, or even to collecting beetles from a dead cow, than to attempt to determine what is happening in the darkness of a hornets' walled nest or in a yellow jackets' underground city.

Time, patience, ingenuity, and a little bravery are necessary for one to become a student of wasps. Bravery we add because the wasps, rather naturally, feel possessive toward their nests and will occasionally assert their rights by inserting their stingers into the human observer. Perhaps it was a wasp fancier who, through experience, coined the phrase, "Don't stir up a hornet's nest." And that is exactly where we started our survey of the wasps.

Part Two

THE BEES

CHAPTER 5

Solitary to Social Bees

God promised the children of Israel a "land that floweth with milk and honey." One of the most profound and far-reaching promises in the history of mankind was thus wrapped up in terms of those two simple foodstuffs. Honey and the bees that produce it are referred to numerous times in the Bible and their worth was obviously appreciated. The bees recognized by man for their value to him since ancient times are the honeybees. The honeybees, however, constitute only four species of bees, and of these one species only is the primary honey producer kept by man. The world is, in fact, full of bees, several thousand species of them, but like the wasps, the great majority of these are solitary insects, a few are subsocial, and fewer yet—a very small percentage of the total—are truly social.

The bees are closely related to one large group of wasps, the sphecoids (not the social wasps) and are really not greatly different from these wasp relatives. It is presumed that far back on the bees' family tree hangs a wasp ancestor from which both the bees and the sphecoid wasps have descended, each evolving along its own path from that point of departure.

The primary difference between wasps and bees is that bees are totally vegetarian in habit. Wasps, except for a rare exception, feed their young on body-building meat—either caught, paralyzed, and stored, or caught, killed, carved, and chewed. The adult wasps sip nectar from the flowers or other sweet juice from various sources, but to this pristine diet they add some body juices from their animal prey. Bees of all kinds—solitary, subsocial, and social—live on nectar and pollen. To help them in this way of life their bodies have developed certain modifications from the basic wasp model. These include a modification of mouthparts to form a long tonguelike structure called the proboscis with which liquid from deep in flowers is obtained. The bees also have numerous body hairs, sometimes branched, to catch and hold pollen as the bee works about the flowers. They also sometimes have special areas on the legs or abdomen designed for carrying loads of pollen. Very importantly, they have also developed highly complex patterns of behavior, which differ from those of the wasps, and which allow them to take advantage of pollen and nectar and to base their economy or way of life upon these products.

As with the wasps, we can survey the various types of solitary bees and see an ascending scale of development toward a social level of living. The solitary bees lead lives much like those of the solitary wasps. Among the least-advanced solitary bees the adult females mate, prepare a nest or cells typical for their species, mass-provision these, lay their eggs, seal the cells, and then leave them. They will never see their young; indeed, in most cases they will be dead before their progeny emerge as adults.

There is one important difference, though, between wasps who follow this pattern of life and the solitary bees. The wasps provision their cells with animal food—that is, with paralyzed spiders and insects. The bees provision theirs with a mixture of pollen and honey. This is usually in the form of a small ball of pollen moistened with nectar. The pollen provides the protein necessary for the growth of the young bee. The larva in its cell eats these provisions, grows, and reaches full larval size. Depending on the time of year—whether it is late in the season or early—and also on the pattern of the species, the larva may pupate and emerge as an adult in the same year or remain suspended in a prepupal state until the following spring, when it undergoes its pupal stage and then emerges to carry on its reproductive activities.

The solitary bees as a group, like the solitary wasps, have taken advantage of a wide range of habitats for establishing their nests. Many of the bees burrow into the soil and prepare there a series of individual cells within which the young develop. Other species, instead of excavating cells, construct them from earth or sand agglutinated together with a salivary secretion. These may be individual cells or several masonry cells grouped together, and they may be placed in a variety of places, as on rocks, walls, and similar locations. Bees constructing such cells are commonly called mason bees.

Still other species make use of existing crevices or holes such as those in plants, walls, or timbers. Some bees even use a snail shell for each baby's home. In the shell the female places the food and an egg, seals the shell securely, and leaves it. A group of bees often found nesting in plant cavities are the leaf-cutting bees. These ingenious creatures, using their mandibles, cut oval pieces from leaves or flowers and fly back to their chosen nest cavity. When sufficient pieces of plant material have been collected and carried to the home site, these pieces are rolled and formed into a thimble-shaped liner for the cavity. On the leafy bed is placed a pollen ball plus an egg. The cell is sealed with more leaf cuttings. The mother then departs.

The building trades are well represented among the solitary bees, for in addition to the excavators and the masons previously mentioned, there are also the carpenters. Carpenter bee is the common name for those solitary species which bore into wood, forming tunnels in which the cells for their young are located. Included in this group are some of the largest of the bees. They may be an inch in length and are heavy-bodied. They are often mistaken for bumblebees. The female, having tunneled some distance into the wood, places a food supply at the end of the tunnel and deposits an egg on it. This cell is then divided off from the rest of the tunnel by the female, who probably uses plant resin to make the partition. Again she provisions, lays a second egg in this new cell, and seals it off. This is repeated until several such cells have been formed. Finally, the whole is sealed and the mother leaves. Within their individual cells the young develop and eventually burrow their way out when their metamorphosis is completed.

Among the bees, carpenters, masons, and excavators there may be, but whereas in the human building trades the males predominate, among the bees it is solely the females who belong. Since only the female bees lay eggs, only they feel any instinctive need to prepare these nests. The males of these species exist to mate with the females. This accomplished, they are of no further consequence in the scheme of the species' development and soon die. From the eggs laid by the cell-constructing females will develop sexually developed males and females for the next of the innumerable series of generations of the species that have lived and that will live in the future.

A curious trait among some solitary bees is the tendency to nest in close proximity to one another. Certain mason bees may at times be found constructing their cells very close together, massing the cells on a wall. Ground-nesting bees may also at times crowd their individual burrows and

Some solitary bees, although not social like honeybees, bumblebees, and stingless bees, do on occasion lay their eggs in close proximity to one another. In this photograph of a cut-away section of soil the young of a nonsocial species of bee are developing. Each larva is curled around a ball of pollen and nectar provided for the young by the mother at the time she deposited the egg, placing it at the end of an earthen tunnel. The mother does not care for the young as it develops; each new adult will make its way to the surface of the soil when its development is complete and environmental conditions are right.

cells among those belonging to others of their species, so that there are formed aggregations or villages of these bees and their nests. At first appearance they would seem to be a group of social insects, busily working together. In reality, they are simply solitary bees crowded together for one reason or another, and the reasons are not always clear. At times there may be a shortage of suitable nesting areas available and the bees are thus forced to crowd themselves. This is obviously not always the case, however, and there must be additional causes. In some cases the females may have returned, following winter hibernation, to the home nest areas where they were born. Another theory is that individuals may be attracted by the scent of others. And we are led to wonder—throwing scientific caution aside—whether there is here perhaps simply a glimmer of some social feeling.

Among the solitary bees forming such aggregations are species belonging to the subfamily Halictinae of the family Halictidae. The halictine bees are interesting because within the confines of this subfamily is found a range of species from solitary to social. Some halictines live in aggregations but each is actually a solitary island amidst a sea of other bees. Others take a step forward, and several females share a common burrow, with each female's brood cells being constructed off the main burrow. In this case the females have only the burrow in common, but through this degree of cooperation each bee has achieved a saving in labor. Some advance beyond this point, and besides sharing a common burrow also pool their resources and work together in preparing cells and in provisioning the cells in the common nest. They also share in guard duty. This duty consists of standing at the entrance to the burrow, the guard's head actually blocking the entrance, to discourage other insects that might prey upon the nest and its occupants. When a nest mate wishes to enter or depart, this guard backs into a wider portion of the burrow. As a result of cooperative living on this level, the nest is guarded by females who evidently share this duty. A measure of rather constant protection is thus achieved, whereas the nest of a strictly solitary species has protection only when the adult female is present.

Several females of the species *Augochloropsis sparsilis* may stay together in the same nest all summer and here a division of labor occurs, with some of the females doing all of the egg laying and others doing all of the nest, foraging, and guard duties. These latter are not workers—that is, they are not a separate caste of females but are physically identical to the egg-laying females. Probably these "working" bees have been fertilized, as were the "queen" or "queens." How this division of labor develops is not completely understood, but it is a real division of labor between adults, and these adults are not necessarily of the same family. This is of significance because, as we stated earlier, among the social insects the society is almost always based upon a family group—the parents, or at least the mother, and the offspring. Some of the halictine bees, therefore, indicate another path that the evolution of some insect societies may have taken.

Finally the Social Register is attained by *Halictus malachurus.* Females of this European species come forth from hibernation in spring and begin housekeeping in old burrows in the soil or excavate new ones. In some cases two or three females will share a burrow, each maintaining her own group of brood cells off the common burrow. Each female mass-provisions her cells and lays her eggs. The female bee, however, does not depart but is still present when her young emerge as adult bees. These are all females but are not identical with their mother in form. They are smaller and vary somewhat in appearance. In fact, before their true origin was determined, these smaller females were classified as members of another genus. These females are sexually undeveloped and do not mate. What is more, at the time of their emergence there are no males with whom to mate. These young, then, are workers and function in this capacity. They prepare brood cells and provision them, while their mother remains in the nest laying eggs. These colonies remain small, with perhaps only a dozen or so workers. Toward the end of the summer the queen lays eggs which develop into males, or into females like herself and unlike the workers produced earlier. Even though males are now present they do not mate with the workers. Instead they mate with the young queens and these young impregnated females enter hibernation for the winter; the old queen, workers, and males die in the autumn.

Another halictine bee, *Lasioglossum marginatum,* is unusual in that its colonies endure for several years, rather than lasting for only a single summer as is the usual case. The queen of this species establishes a nest and her eggs produce females only, oftentimes for four years in succession. These function as workers. In the last year of her life the queen produces in addition to the usual females some eggs that develop into males. It is reported that when mature males are present, the nests, normally closed at that particular time of the year, are opened, and the males depart to enter other nests of the species that have also been opened to allow the departure of their males. Within these nests the guest males mate with the females found there. These impregnated females hibernate and start colonies the following spring. It may be that all the females are alike but that males are not available to many of them, as during the years the nests are not opened, and they therefore are never fertilized. The members of these long-lasting colonies, both the queen and her daughters, hibernate through unfavorable seasons.

We have been following the evolutionary path as represented in the subfamily Halictinae. Some interesting differences in behavior are shown by bees of the genus *Allodape* in the subfamily Xylocopinae of the family Apidae. The female *Allodape* establishes her nest within a hollow in a plant and lays her eggs, but she does not place these in separate cells. When the larvae emerge, they lie together in the cavity. Depending on the species, the larvae may feed on food stores placed among them, they may be fed regurgitated food when small and given solids later, or they may each be given food each day. Thus we see progressive provisioning among these bees, which is a change from the usual mass provisioning among the solitary and subsocial bees. In *Allodape* there is physical contact between adults and young, but there is none in *Halictus* or among solitary bees whose young develop within sealed cells. The *Allodape* female may establish a nest alone, or several females, all sisters, may stay in their home nest and all lay eggs. The young from these eggs are cared for as a group by all the females. Thus there is no queen, all females being egg layers, and there are no workers as such, all females working, but there is a working and living together of adult bees. These bees are considered subsocial, there being no division of labor.

Generally small and unobtrusive, the solitary bees and their semisocial and barely social cousins carry on their lives, little noticed by man and probably little noticing man. Not so our next group of bees.

CHAPTER 6

The Cycle of the Bumblebees

Few there are who would argue the right-of-way with a bumblebee. Bumblebees are among the most imposing in appearance of all bees. They are heavybodied, hairy, and brightly marked, usually with a black and yellow or black and white pattern. They are capable of inflicting a decidedly uncomfortable sting but are not unduly aggressive. They will, however, readily move to the defense of their nest. We once spent four hours digging up a colony of bumblebees and only one sting was sustained by the group of diggers and spectators. However, we were aided by one small boy with a butterfly net swinging on those bees moving in too close, we did use chloroform to stun the bees remaining in the nest, and we did all duck (and even run) rather frequently.

Bumblebees are social—much more so than the most socially evolved of the halictine bees, but less so than two other groups of bees, the stingless bees and the honeybees. The bumblebees are widely distributed; they are found in Europe, Asia, both North and South America, but in Africa only north of the Sahara Desert. They are more numerous in temperate zones than in the tropics and are found from the southernmost part of South America to within the Arctic Circle, where their annual colonies are short, hurried, but successful affairs during the brief summers.

Following a pattern made familiar to us by the social wasps and by some of the less social bees, the bumblebee queen mates in the fall and hibernates. This hibernation is usually underground and lasts until the following spring. When she emerges, for some time she flies about from flower to flower, eating well while her ovaries develop. She is also searching for a proper place in which to start her nest.

Bumblebees are ground dwellers, with some species typically nesting in the ground and other species nesting on the ground. The queens may choose to start their nests in clumps of dry grass, or they may take over the abandoned nest of a mouse or other small mammal and burrow into the nesting material already provided by the former occupant. The queen shapes and works with the nesting material until a small cavity is formed and here she rests, emerging from time to time to drink nectar and eat pollen from the flowers within the area.

Well fed, the queen's body begins to produce wax, which is secreted as thin scales both dorsally and ventrally through the joints separating the hard, chitinous, overlapping plates, known as sclerites, which cover her

The bumblebees—black, marked with yellow or white—are among the most attractive of the bees. They do not construct combs but live amidst an irregular collection of old cocoons from which adult bees have emerged. These empty cocoons are then used as containers for pollen and small amounts of honey.

abdomen. The wax scales are removed from the surface of the abdomen by the legs and then manipulated and worked by the mandibles. Using this amazing product the queen builds inside the nest entrance a small container known as a honey pot. She begins to collect nectar, returns to the nest with it, and regurgitates it from her crop, an enlarged portion of her foregut, into the honey pot. The honey in this pot is a reserve supply for the queen's use in case of bad weather during her colony founding and will also be used as food by the first young when they are newly emerged as adults.

At about the same time that the honey storing is taking place the queen also begins constructing the first cell for her eggs. This, too, is composed of wax, and it is built in the center of the small nest cavity. The queen now begins to collect pollen, in addition to her regular nectar collecting. The pollen, moistened with nectar, is formed into a ball, and the waxen egg cell may be built on top of this ball, or the pollen may be packed into the bottom of the cell after it is constructed. In either case, the queen then lays six to twelve eggs on top of the pollen and seals the cell with more wax. The egg cell is actually a very small structure, being only about ¼ inch or slightly more in diameter. The honey pot, also, is Lilliputian, being approximately ¾ inch in height and ½ inch in diameter.

Within the cell the eggs develop. In a few days, probably four or five, the larvae emerge from the eggs and begin literally to eat their bed, that is, the pollen on which they find themselves. In addition to eating their pollen mattress, the larvae are fed by the queen. Depending on the species, there are two methods by which the larvae are fed. In one group, the pollen storers (which store pollen in separate containers in the nest), the queen makes an opening in the cell with her mandibles—or in some species the cell is left partially open—and from time to time she regurgitates into the cell a mixture of nectar and pollen so that the larvae are sitting in their supper as they eat it. In other species, known as pocket makers, pockets of pollen are placed within the walls of the cells and the larvae feed primarily upon the floor of pollen and upon the pollen in the pockets located in the walls about them.

Regardless of the manner in which they are fed, the larvae eat and grow, molting their old skins periodically as these become too tight. The wax cell, originally constructed to contain only pollen and eggs, now must be stretched to enclose the growing larvae, and so the queen occasionally incorporates additional wax to expand it. As the end of the larval period

Among the bumblebees, small waxen egg cells, as in the center of the picture, are constructed on the sides of cocoons. Within the cell the queen lays several eggs. As the larvae produced from the eggs grow, additional wax is added to the cell to increase its dimensions. Eventually each young forms a cocoon about itself, after which the workers strip away the enclosing wax, using it elsewhere.

approaches, bulges along the cell walls show the positions of the individual larvae. In the pocket-making species each larva does not have a private cell, as is the usual case with the wasps and with most of the solitary and subsocial bees; the bumblebee larvae up to this point have been all together in a common cell. However, some of the pollen-storing species have larvae that separate from their neighbors early in the larval stage, each coming to occupy a distinct cell.

As is also the case with the social wasps, the digestive system of the bumblebee larva is not complete; during the larval period no waste materials have been voided. This would seem to be particularly important for the bumblebee larvae, which must often share a community bed and at least some of which have their food simply squirted into bed with and around them. As the larvae become pupae, the connection within their digestive system becomes complete, and the wastes are excreted.

Each larva spins about itself a yellowish, silken, egg-shaped cocoon, so that each is separated from her sisters during her pupal stage. While the young are thus involved in their silent transformation, each in the dark of her own silken quarters, the queen removes the remains of the waxen cell which originally enclosed the group. Now a clump of cocoons is exposed. The wax which has been removed will be reused. The queen may employ it in building another egg cell; in some species, it may be used to build a waxen canopy raised above the cocoons; or, in others, eventually an entire cover about the nest area may be built of wax with grass and other nesting material incorporated into it.

Throughout this process the queen has been more a servant than a queen, for she has been working hard—producing wax, building with it, laying eggs, and feeding herself and her young. In addition to all this she has actually been incubating the brood. From a bird we expect this, but it seems strange indeed to imagine a bee sitting, or rather lying, on her eggs,

The photographer, by removing half the cocoon covering, exposed this bumblebee pupa. The pupal stage is a time of transformation from the wormlike larva to the adult. Much of the change has taken place with this individual. Its main body parts are formed, but it has not yet attained the coloring of the adult.

larvae, and pupae. This the queen does, however, for the first brood, to give them the warmth needed for their development. She does leave them for fairly lengthy periods in order to collect food. As the overall size of the brood increases through the growth of each individual, the queen's body is no longer sufficient to cover the whole. She remains in the center and a groove actually develops in the brood where she lies. The warmth from her body causes the young in the center to develop more rapidly than those on the perimeter and so the centrally located individuals emerge as adults first. The metamorphosis completed, each adult cuts a circular piece from the top of her cocoon, often being aided in this by the queen, and emerges to dry her coat, sip honey from the honey pot, and gain her strength. Within two or three days these newly produced females will fill the role of workers in the colony.

Even as these first young are developing the queen makes preparations for producing more. Near the top of one of the cocoons she constructs her second waxen egg cell and on other cocoons she may start additional ones, thus initiating the cycle again. However, with the second and later broods, the incubation of the young will not be so important or necessary, for previously produced broods will be creating considerable warmth through the metabolism of their rich food supply. After the first brood emerge as adults they will take over much of the work of food collecting and caring for the later young. The queen, although she usually soon ceases to forage, may continue to do some work within the nest, never becoming simply an egg-laying automaton as is the case with some social-insect queens. It is thought that she alone constructs each of the egg cells in which she lays the eggs.

The bumblebee queen practices, all unbeknownst to herself, a most effective program of planned parenthood. All egg cells, with the exception of the first, are placed upon cocoons which contain pupae. This timing is important, for by the time the larvae in the new cell are in need of food, the older brood, one of which had spun the cocoon base of the larvae's home, will have emerged to help care for their younger, hungry sisters. And so it continues, throughout the history of the colony. As the colony develops the queen begins laying more eggs in each cell and gradually increases her total egg output. The number of eggs laid in an egg cell has been found to be proportionate to the number of pupae developing within the brood on which the eggs were laid—each time there being more eggs laid than the number of brood on which they rest. Effective provision is thereby made for an increasing population with an adequate household staff to build, provision, and babysit the increasingly larger broods of young.

The comb of the bumblebee nest is actually largely composed of old cocoons that are built one upon another, expanding outward and upward, depending on the confines of the nest. Once the occupants of the cocoons have emerged, some of the cocoons are used for storage of food; others are simply left, or may be cut away, or are crushed by the weight above them. Over the comb may be a wax canopy with nesting material worked into it, or this material may encircle the whole comb with entrances through the wax. Additional nesting material, such as grasses, may be worked into the general area about the nest. Depending upon the species, the complete comb of a colony, near the end of the season, may vary from a few inches in diameter to the size of a man's head or slightly larger. The individuals in the colony may number from less than a hundred up to a thousand or occasionally to two thousand in a very successful colony, though a few hundred is a more normal population.

Since the bumblebee colony is destined to survive only one season, its workers do not need to lay in large food stores, as do the honeybee workers, which must store food to carry their colony through the winter. Bumblebees do, nevertheless, store some food in the nest. For this storage, they do not construct neat, hexagonal, wax cells as the honeybees do but simply use the empty cocoons that made up the bulk of their nest. The arrangement is less organized and the cleanliness is less than that attained by the honeybees, but the oval-shaped cocoons serve the storage purpose very well and are much more economical than the pure wax cells of the honeybees, which represent a large investment on the part of the colony. Some bumblebees may also construct a few wax containers about the periphery of the comb, in which nectar is stored for brief periods.

The ragged tops of the empty cocoons in the bumblebee colony are neatly trimmed by the workers and may have a wax edge or extension added to them. Workers return from foraging with nectar in their crops and regurgitate the nectar into these food-storage cocoons. Through the evaporation of water the nectar gradually thickens and becomes honey. These cells may then be covered with a wax cap.

The workers also forage for pollen. This usually yellow, powdery substance is not swallowed but is packed into "pollen baskets," located on the bees' hind legs. As the bee crawls down into the center of a flower to drink nectar, the long hairs on her body become covered with the flower's pollen. Using her legs the bee rubs this pollen from her body toward her head, where she moistens it with nectar. The moistened pollen is then passed back to her hind legs. On the outer surface of each of these two legs is the pollen basket, which consists of a smooth, concave area of the leg surrounded by long, stiff hairs. A foraging bee may often be seen flying about with two large yellow lumps on her hind legs. This is the load of pollen with which she will return to the nest.

Bumblebees have two main ways of storing pollen in their nests, as we noted briefly in discussing the feeding of the brood. Species known as pollen storers store in empty cocoons the pollen they bring home. These old cocoons are sometimes extended by the addition of wax until they are between 2 and 3 inches in height. A pollen-laden forager on returning to the nest will stand with her head away from the old cocoon, now destined to become a pollen receptacle, and with a movement of her middle leg remove the pollen load from her hind leg, pushing it into the receptacle. The second method is used by the pocket makers, species which have pockets for pollen on the sides of the wax cell in which the larvae are developing. The workers in this group, when returning with pollen, store it in these pockets, unless there are no developing larvae in the nest, in which case it may be stored in empty cocoons, as with the pollen-storing species.

In a well-established bumblebee nest a rather constant temperature is maintained, and this may be several degrees above the surrounding air temperature. The developing brood digesting its food produces heat, as do also the adult workers carrying on their activities within the nest. The wax canopy or envelope, when present, and the vegetation used as nesting material about the comb serve as insulation and aid in temperature control. Occasionally the temperature may become too high, and then workers will fan with their wings to create a cooling air movement.

The nest is protected by its location, by the canopy and other material surrounding it, but especially by the stings of the workers. The bumblebee sting pierces the skin of the adversary and venom is then forced through the sting into the unlucky victim. The bumblebee can withdraw her sting to sting again, although her venom supply will become temporarily exhausted after she has stung a few times in succession. The bumblebee may also eject her liquid rectal contents at her enemy, shooting it for a distance of several inches, and she is known to bite when disturbed.

From the modest beginnings provided by the queen bumblebee, then, there has developed by midpoint in the colony's history a good-sized nest, housing developing young, inhabited by numerous adult offspring, containing food stores, possessed of a fairly efficient heating and cooling system, and defended by an effective, sting-wielding, totally feminine army.

CHAPTER 7

Organization of Bumblebee Colonies

Sex is one aspect of life that the social insects have well under control. The majority of the members of the colony are seldom diverted by it, since they are underdeveloped sexually. These are, of course, the workers. The queen carries out the reproductive functions for the entire colony. And finally the production of new sexual forms is concentrated into a brief period, produced in a single insect extravaganza.

The strength of a bumblebee colony lies in its workers, who carry out the activities involved in day-to-day living. To carry out these duties a division of labor is developed in colonies containing sufficient workers. The main duties of workers are foraging, nest duty, including care of the young and of the nest, and guard duty. It has been found that commonly the larger workers do the foraging and the smaller workers remain in the nest to carry out jobs there, although there are many exceptions to this rule. Logically (by human logic, that is) this division according to size would seem to be a most practical arrangement. The larger ones can carry bigger loads of pollen and nectar than can their smaller sisters. The latter are better suited by their size to move about in the rather close quarters of the nest.

Bumblebees form habits that, as with people, evidently make their duties easier to perform. A bee that carries out nest duties often continues to do this rather consistently. One that begins to forage forms this habit and oftentimes continues to forage. She may remain constant to a particular kind of flower for a period of time. While bees often collect both nectar and pollen on one trip, a bee may collect only pollen or only nectar for a number of trips, until for some reason her pattern is broken. Even the choice of cells in which to deposit nectar or pollen may remain constant for several trips. What the individual forager collects and the amounts collected probably depend upon a number of factors, including her habits, her size, the size and age of the brood—that is, what the food needs of the colony are—and what supplies are currently stored within the nest. It may be that in wandering about over the comb when she returns to the nest to discharge her load, the forager becomes alerted to the needs of the colony and to some extent patterns her collecting accordingly.

The nest workers carry out a variety of duties. They feed the young. They secrete wax and mold it and other wax already in the colony into honey pots, extensions of old cocoons, expansions in larval cells, pockets for pollen storage in some species, canopies or envelopes, and seals for cocoons filled with honey. They arrange nesting material, fan, help incubate the brood, pack pollen into containers, help young adults emerge from their cocoons, and clean and prepare old cocoons for food storage.

A less common job carried out by some bumblebees is guard duty. Here again individual bees often remain faithful to the job once they have established its practice. A guard tends to stand her duty in one area, as in one section of the entrance tunnel. She may remain guard for several hours at a time, after which she may carry out other duties, such as foraging, and later return to her position as security officer. Apparently, only the larger and more prosperous colonies can afford to divert workers from more essential tasks to guard duty.

The division of labor in a bumblebee colony is thus not a static thing. If a particular need arises a worker can change her job. There is obviously no lack of work for the bumblebee workers, and the old axiom "busy as a bee" certainly applies to them. They wear themselves out in a short time, often living only three to eight weeks.

As we have indicated, bumblebee workers are often of varying sizes. The first young produced in a colony are entirely dependent upon the queen's ability to house and feed them. Probably they are underfed, or at least are not fed liberally, and their quarters within the wax cell are likely to be cramped, for the queen must secrete all the wax that goes into its construction. These first workers would therefore tend to be undernourished, underdeveloped sexually, and small in size. Later broods of young mature under more propitious circumstances, with workers to help feed them and to secrete wax for larger larval cells. Therefore later workers tend to be larger than their older sisters. However, the greatest range in size of workers is found among the pocket-making bumblebees. Recall that the larvae of the pocket makers share a common cell and feed upon pollen stored in pockets in the side of the wax cell. The lucky babies that grow up next to these pockets find food readily available; the other larvae find themselves pushed back from the table and no doubt have less to eat than their strategically placed sisters. As a result, in worker broods of pocket-making bumblebees there is an obvious gradation in size.

As the summer season advances, ever-increasing numbers of workers are available in a prospering colony to care for and feed the brood liberally. The colony then reaches a successful climax by producing sexual forms, rather than more workers. Males develop from unfertilized eggs; queens, like workers, from fertilized eggs. It is thought that virgin queens rather than workers develop simply because of the abundance of food provided them by a sufficient worker force. Among the pocket makers, who serve themselves from the pockets, it would seem that some females would still be short-changed on the food and fail to develop properly. However, in at least one species of pocket maker, observers have found that the brood slated to become sexually developed is fed solely by regurgitation and that no pockets are present in their cells. This may also be the case in other species, or the sexual brood may receive regurgitated food in addition to that stored in the pockets. In either case sufficient food is evidently provided for their complete development. If it is truly the case, then, that queen production among the bumblebees is dependent upon sufficient food being available to the brood, queen production has a far simpler explanation with the bumblebees than with the honeybees and most other social insects, as we shall note eventually.

In regard to reproductive forms, a bumblebee colony may produce only males, only virgin queens, or both. The males are usually produced slightly in advance of the queens. The newly emerged males stay in the colony for three or four days, feeding on the stored food. Eventually they fly out of the nest, and often do not return, but simply wait or fly about searching for mates and resting on foliage.

The virgin queens upon emergence from their cocoons may stay in the nest for a time and may even help with household duties or do some foraging. Eventually they leave the nest, mate with the waiting males, and soon search for a suitable place in which to hibernate. In temperate climates they alone will survive the winter.

There is a basic difference between these young queens and the workers.

Provided with plenty of food, the queens develop the organs known as the fat bodies, which store resources for their hibernation. These fat reserves do not develop in the workers even though they too may have more than ample food provided them. And, as with the temperate-area wasps, abundant food in the fall causes the bumblebee queen to store nourishment but does not cause her ovaries to develop. The ovaries do not become functional until the following spring.

In temperate climates, once sexual forms have been produced by a colony, no more workers are produced and the colony begins to decline. Even though ideal conditions for rearing sexual forms may have been attained very early in the season and these forms have subsequently been produced, their appearance marks the beginning of the end for that colony. The young queens thus produced will even enter hibernation in the middle of the summer and remain there until the following spring. In the tropics, however, colonies are perennial and do not break down at the end of a season. Whereas many wasps have hibernating queens in temperate zones, but in the tropics often establish new colonies by swarming, this does not appear to be the case with the bumblebees. New bumblebee colonies in the tropics are thought to be initiated by queens which establish them working alone.

Although it appears that the bumblebees have sex neatly categorized and relegated to the queen, there are exceptions. If a queen is removed or lost from a colony, certain of the workers will attempt to take over her position, building egg cells and laying unfertilized eggs that give rise to males. One of these bumblebee workers becomes the dominant individual in the colony and there may be others that occupy the positions of second and third dominants. The degree of dominance is apparently directly correlated with the development of the ovaries. Egg-laying workers may be present in the colony even when there is a queen. This condition, if it develops, often occurs at about the time that sexual broods are being reared. Throughout the life of the colony the queen evidently displays her dominance. She alone constructs the egg cells in which she lays eggs, and when necessary she protects her newly laid eggs against workers which may try to eat them. Just why workers are more successful at egg laying at the climax of the colony is not clear. Perhaps the amount of food available is a factor; perhaps the colony has reached a size which makes it difficult for the queen to be in complete control; perhaps the queen is simply worn out. An interesting piece of research disclosed that those workers with more highly developed ovaries are also most pugnacious, rushing readily to the defense of the nest.

There are plenty of creatures against whom the colony must be defended. Larger animals may at least occasionally prey upon bumblebee colonies; these include mice, which may eat the first brood when it is not protected, skunks, and badgers. The bumblebee nest is home to a wide variety of invertebrates which may simply use the nest for protection, may feed upon stored food, a brood, a comb, or incidental organic matter; or may actually live on or within the bees themselves. These lesser creatures include various flies, beetles, moths, and mites. This pattern of an insect colony providing home and food for many other living things is one that we shall see throughout the realm of the social insects.

As occurs with human beings, some of the bumblebees' most troublesome and expensive guests are others of their own kind. All true bumblebees are of the genus *Bombus.* There is another genus of bumblebee, *Psithyrus,* the members of which are commonly called cuckoo bumblebees and are parasitic on their *Bombus* relatives. The name cuckoo, as used for these bees, refers to the European birds of that name, which lay their eggs in other birds' nests and then leave eggs and parental responsibilities behind, relying upon the owners of the nests to rear these foreign bird children.

Each species of *Psithyrus* bumblebee parasitizes one particular species or at most a few specific species of *Bombus.* A *Psithyrus* queen, upon finding a colony of *Bombus* of the correct species, enters it. Once within, she lays her eggs, and these and the resulting brood are cared for by the unsuspecting *Bombus* workers. From her eggs develop males and fertile females. No *Psithyrus* workers are produced, for this genus, by exploiting the *Bombus* workers, has no need for workers of its own. So far removed from having to fend for their young are the *Psithyrus* bees that they have no pollen baskets on their legs and so cannot carry home the baby food as do their *Bombus* servants. Once the fertile *Psithyrus* forms emerge, they mate, the females hibernate, and the next summer these enter *Bombus* colonies to repeat the story.

For the *Psithyrus* female to enter a *Bombus* nest is not easy. Usually the workers attempt to repel her, and many bees may be killed in the process—sometimes including the invader. The *Psithyrus* female, however, has a harder, heavier body covering than the *Bombus,* her sting is more powerful, and her jaws are built as more effective weapons. It is thought that she may enter a nest secretly and hide until her body absorbs the odor of the nest so that she is not detected as an intruder. The *Psithyrus* females do not emerge from hibernation as early as their host species; rather they emerge when the *Bombus* species has had time to establish a colony. The *Psithyrus* probably attempts her entry when the host colony has had time to become well established but is still small enough to give her a fighting chance. Just what fate befalls the *Bombus* queen is not always certain. Perhaps she is sometimes killed by the *Psithyrus* queen. In some cases both females have been known to remain in the nest. However, once the *Bombus* colony has been parasitized few or no more *Bombus* workers seem to be produced, very few if any males, and no queens. The *Psithyrus* female may eat the *Bombus* eggs or in some way prevent the queen from laying.

Even among the *Bombus,* there are certain species in which a queen will occasionally attempt to invade an already established colony of her own species or sometimes even of a closely related species. If successful, she kills the rightful queen and replaces her in that position. Probably in many such cases the second *Bombus* queen has emerged from hibernation later than the queen that has already established the colony. The invader may come upon one of these colonies when searching for a suitable nest site and simply move in, although the place is already occupied.

Bumblebees recognize their nest mates by their odor and hence detect invaders by their incorrect odors. It is thought that each species of bumblebee may have its own hereditary odor, but evidently there is also a nest odor, compounded from a variety of sources within the nest, which the bees absorb. Each colony then probably has its own distinctive odor, but this odor is more similar to that of others of their own species than to that of other species.

Something is lacking among the bumblebees. That is the mutual feeding of the members of the colony, the trophallaxis that we noted among the wasps. So far as is known, bumblebee larvae do not produce any pay for their food; indeed many of them are closed off from the adults. They receive but do not give. Nor do the adult bumblebees feed one another directly. They forage for themselves or feed from the mutual stores kept in the nests. Their odor badge helps to organize the colony, but one is led to wonder why they are thus organized. What direct motivation moves them now, or moved them in the past, to live in societies where many of them literally work themselves to death for the good of the community?

CHAPTER 8

Stingless Bees

Living things sometimes take strange turnings along the evolutionary path. These may ultimately lead them to success or doom them to failure. One such bypath taken by certain bees was the loss of the sting or its reduction to a vestigial organ. A bee without a functional sting seems about as likely as a rattlesnake without a rattle, but certain rattlesnakes living on some islands in the Gulf of California have evolved beyond the rattle and are indeed rattleless rattlesnakes. And so we come to the stingless bees.

Stingless bees live only in the tropics and subtropics and consist of over 200 species grouped into two principal genera, the *Melipona* and *Trigona*. Species of *Melipona* are found only in the New World tropics and contain some species that are as large as small honeybees. Species of *Trigona* are found in the tropics of both the Old World and the New World. Within this genus are some species as large as the larger *Melipona,* but most are small, including some that are only ⅛ inch in length.

These bees would seem to have thrown away a valuable heritage in the loss of the functional sting, but they have developed other attributes which more than compensate for the lacking weapon. When a colony of stingless bees is disturbed, the inhabitants rush out in great numbers and swarm over the person or other creature disturbing them. They crawl over their enemy, biting sharply and repeatedly, and smearing all about a sticky secretion. A few species even use a caustic secretion which causes much discomfort to human skin. Some colonies of these stingless bees contain only a few individuals, but others have been estimated as having 80,000 members. To have such an enormous colony, or even one less than half that size, crawling about over one, nipping and smearing, can be a very unpleasant experience for the attacked and a very successful defensive measure for the attackers.

These bees may build nests in a variety of places—in the open, in holes in the ground, in hollows in trees, in stone walls, in other crevices, on cliffs, or in other similar locations. Some even build in old ant and termite nests.

The basic building material of the stingless bees is wax that is secreted from the upper side of the abdomen. The wax is combined with other materials, such as resin and earth; the resulting product is known as cerumen. If the nest is in a cavity the area may be scaled down to a proper size by walling off parts of the space with sheets of this material. When nests are built in exposed locations they are surrounded by layers of cerumen or other such protective materials. The entrance to stingless-bee nests may be simply a small opening through this outer covering. Especially in nests in cavities, however, the entrance to the nest is through constructed entrance tunnels, which may be from one to several inches in length.

Within the nest are constructed wax combs in which the young are reared. In most species the cells are built in horizontal layers, the cells opening upward. When the first comb is nearing its maximum desired size, a second comb is built above it, supported by wax pillars resting on the first comb. Such a pillar is constructed upward; a cell is built atop it, other cells are built adjoining the first, and thus gradually with the addition of more pillars and cells the comb grows. Wasps hang their combs, building down, and dangle their young upside down, whereas the stingless bees—more logically, it seems to us—build up from the bottom and point their young in the proper direction. Several combs may thus be built by the bees, one above the other, with spaces for traffic left here and there in the combs. Other species may arrange their combs so that they ascend in a spiral. About these brood cells the bees oftentimes construct a protective, insulating involucrum, or envelope of thin sheets of cerumen. A few species, considered to be more primitive, instead of building horizontal combs simply arrange their cells in small groups; these bees are known as cluster makers. No wax involucrum is built around the cells in the cluster-maker nests.

The stingless bees store food in the nest but keep the food supplies separate from the brood. Using their mixture of wax and extraneous materials, they construct oval pots for nectar and pollen and arrange these in groups

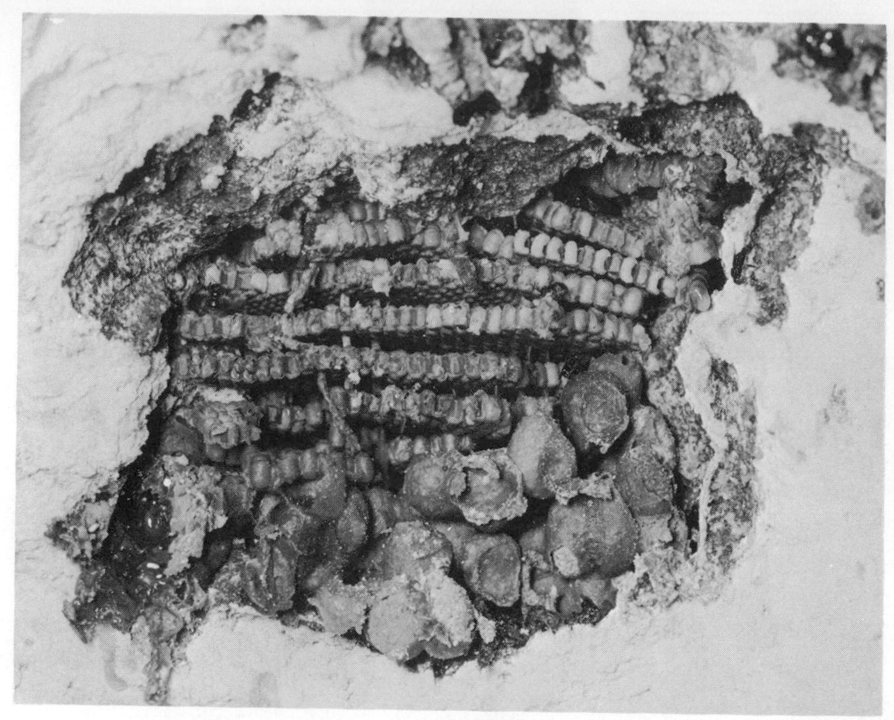

By breaking away a piece of rock on a cliff face, this stingless-bee nest was exposed. The layers of cells are built one above another, and the cells open upward. The walls of some cells were removed by the photographer, and the developing young can be seen in them. At the bottom of the nest are containers constructed by the bees. Some of these, such as the one torn open at bottom center, contain pollen. Others are filled with honey, and the honey from a broken container gleams in the left corner of the photograph.

at the sides of, or below the combs. These containers may be alike or different; in some species the pollen containers are tall cylinders, while the honey pots are oval. One African species constructs hexagonal storage pots.

Like their solitary ancestors, and unlike most other social insects, the stingless bees mass-provision their brood cells. When a cell is completed it is provisioned with pollen and honey. On the provisions the queen lays an egg and the cell is then closed with wax by one of the workers. Within this cell the young bee undergoes its complete metamorphosis from egg to larva, to pupa, to adult, finally emerging in its adult form. Once the cocoon about the pupa has been spun, the workers strip away much of the wax cell that encloses it, reusing the wax elsewhere, and allowing the adult to emerge more easily. The brood cells are thus used only a single time. In two Australian species, the method of provisioning the cells is somewhat different. The brood cell is about half filled with food, the egg is laid, and some additional food is later given to the larva before the cell is sealed.

In stingless bees of the genus *Trigona,* male bees, produced from unfertilized eggs, are reared in normal-sized brood cells, such as those used for raising workers; special larger cells are built for rearing queens. Since the queens also develop in sealed cells, their development cannot be modified by a special diet or by glandular secretions fed to them by the workers. However, the large cells in which they develop provide room for plentiful food supplies—more food, certainly, than is provided for those young destined to be workers. In these particular stingless bees, then, the decisive factor in the production of queens rather than workers from fertilized eggs, is thought to be simply an abundance of food.

In the genus *Melipona,* queen production is not so readily explained, for in this genus the queens develop in cells the same size as those provided for workers and males. The queens emerge from cells scattered randomly about the combs; they do not come from any special section. So far as can be determined, no special food is provided for them, and the size of the cells precludes any possibility of extra food supplies being given them. The theory has therefore been proposed, and research appears to support it, that caste is hereditary in these particular bees. Researchers have found that the ratio of queens to workers is that which would be expected if caste is indeed a heritable trait. Many more queens are produced in *Melipona* than in the stingless bees which raise queens in special large cells. It is thought that some of these queens may be killed to prevent such an abundance as would place undue strain on the resources of the colony.

The queens of the stingless bees differ from the workers in some significant ways. They do not have pollen baskets. They cannot produce wax. Their heads and eyes are smaller than their worker sisters'. The queens are thus unfit for founding colonies unaided, as do bumblebee queens. Stingless-bee colonies are therefore founded by swarming.

Workers find a suitable location for a new nest and begin work on it. Eventually a young queen from the mother colony joins them. At least in one species, only then does she set forth on a mating flight, returning to her new home, and finally starting the production of eggs. The mother colony may help support the new colony for a period of a few weeks. Colored honey experimentally placed in the mother colony has been found transferred to the daughter colony during these beginning stages.

Colonies of these bees, it is believed, may last several years; since they live in warm areas there is no winter to cause their cessation. Probably there is in each colony only the one egg-laying queen, but with young queens present awaiting the proper time and conditions for setting up new colonies. Whether these bees have any means of replacing a worn-out or aged queen, or whether the colony must die with its queen, is not known with any certainty.

Stingless bees sometimes build their nests among rocks and in crevices. The entrance to such a nest is often a tunnel constructed by the bees. Guard bees station themselves at the entrance to defend the colony and alert its members to danger. Although stingless, these bees bite effectively, sometimes produce an offensive odor, and swarm about the human intruder, becoming disturbingly entangled in one's hair. Their defense is a very effective one.

The workers, it appears, attend to the many jobs about the nest when young, becoming foragers outside the nest when older. This rough division of work according to age on the part of the workers is also found among the honeybees. Within the nest stingless-bee workers build, provision cells, seal cells that contain eggs, care for the queen, clean, receive nectar from the foragers, and act as guards. If the entrance to a stingless-bee colony is very small, it may be blocked by the head of a guard bee, which is withdrawn to allow the passage of authorized traffic. Where the entrance is considerably larger many guard bees may gather. A long entrance tube is a trademark of many of these colonies, and the opening of this tube may be an inch or thereabouts in diameter. Commonly one may see several guard bees lined up along the edge of this opening, all facing outward, stingless but nonetheless appearing dauntless.

The "dance" communication system of the honeybees is famous, and the stingless bees also show evidence of a communication system, although of a simpler type, which is used to advise nest mates of good food sources. When a successful forager returns to the nest, she runs about excitedly. The motion excites other bees and while they do not receive any specific information from the movements of the forager, they do obtain from her body the scent of the crop she has found. In two species of *Melipona,* according to recent findings, sound is produced by the flight muscles in the thorax during this running about. The duration of the individual sound impulses depends upon the distance to the food source, and this may relay a type of information to the forager's nest mates. The sounds are probably received as vibrations through a surface by receptors on the bees' legs. They are not received as air waves. The forager's audience, having been alerted, leaves the hive and searches for the food source. Some species of stingless bees, however, go beyond this level of communication. In these the forager, using a secretion from the mandibular glands, leaves scent marks on the ground or foliage. She thus produces a scent trail from the hive to the food source that nest mates, alerted by her running about in the hive, can then follow.

As with the bumblebees, a number of small creatures find living in stingless-bee colonies to their advantage. Although there are no parasitic stingless bees, one of their own cousins may cause havoc with their nests. This bee is *Lestrimelitta limao,* and it lives a life of theft. Stingless bees of other species may occasionally steal from their relatives but evidently *L. limao* is unable to live in any other way. In fact, these workers do not have pollen baskets for collecting their own stores. Instead they enter their relatives' nests and steal what they need, including honey, pollen (which is carried in the crop), and building materials. They then carry their loot back to their own nests.

The thieves do not easily walk away with whatever they desire; the rightful owners attempt to protect their nest. However, the *L. limao* workers have scent glands that produce a strong odor in the attacked colony. When the natural colony odor is overpowered by this, the guard bees evidently become confused and unable to recognize which bees are enemies and which are nest mates, and thus the defense of the colony is breached. The bee war may continue intermittently over a period as long as a month. The attacked colony may only be crippled, or it may be destroyed. Occasionally the attacked bees turn the tables and later become the attackers. Or the successful *L. limao* may be subsequently attacked and destroyed by another colony.

The honeybee, *Apis mellifera,* did not occur naturally in the New World, but was brought here by man. Consequently the people native to the Americas did not have its honey. However, some of the stingless bees were long ago discovered by the Mayas and kept for their honey. Colonies were housed in lengths of hollow logs and the honey drained out twice a year. The stingless bees do not produce the quantity of honey that honeybees do; they do not arrange it so neatly; nor are they as particular about their sources of liquids, sometimes being found on dead animals and similar materials. But we, like the Mayas, would probably not be too particular, either, if we lived in a sugarless world.

CHAPTER 9

Species of Honeybees

Honeybees come from oxen—or so at least some of the ancients believed. A long-lived superstition held that a swarm of bees could be created by following certain directions. A building containing a door and four windows, one window to each side, was to be prepared. Into it was to be taken a fat ox of about two years of age. Men were to set upon the ox with clubs and beat it to death, pulverizing both flesh and bones without shedding blood. Where blood did accidentally flow the holes were to be stopped with clean cloths. The herb thyme was to be scattered about, and the dead animal left in the room, which was to be immediately sealed shut. After three weeks the building was to be opened for a brief period and then resealed. Eleven days later the building was to be opened once again, and behold—swarms of bees would await. (No mention is made of the odor that would await.) A suffumigation of thyme was to be prepared to draw the swarms from the room into the apiary. The kings (certainly no one considered giving a female credit for being the important individual around whom the colony revolved) were produced from the brain of the ox. The honeybees were not alone in being so marvelously spontaneously generated; wasps and hornets were generated from horses, and asses produced beetles. Another version attributed hornets to mules and wasps to asses. There were people, however, who did not subscribe to these beliefs. Some of these contended rather that bees obtained their young from flowers or by mixing flowers in their mouths. Bees, of course, obtain their young from eggs which come from a queen bee, but that story is only slightly less miraculous (and certainly has a better odor about it) than the story of their spontaneous generation from decaying flesh.

In accord with the general pattern of social insects, the honeybees live in large family groups. There is only one permanent fertile female in each colony, and she produces all the young. Drones or males, and young fertile females or unmated queens, are present in the colony at certain times. The bulk of the colony, however, is composed of the workers, who are stunted, unmated females. The workers devote themselves to the good of the colony, caring for the young produced by the queen, building the nest, storing food, protecting the colony, and carrying on all the other duties that contribute to the welfare of the group as a whole.

We of the Western world are familiar with the so-called domesticated honeybee, *Apis mellifera*. Actually, man has not domesticated the honeybee in the sense of taming it. He has simply made adaptations himself to the needs of the honeybees, providing them with conveniences, such as hives, so that the bees are benefited, and hence man is also able to derive benefits from them.

Honeybee colonies normally nest within man-made hives, in hollows in trees, or other such locations. Within these enclosed areas they build combs from pure wax secreted by their bodies. Within the cells of the combs are reared the young, proceeding from egg to larva, to pupa, to adult. Also within certain of the wax cells is stored the bees' food supply. As the honeybees store large quantities of food—that is, honey—they have been of value and thereby of interest to humans since Stone Age man first collected this golden delicacy. Bumblebees store small amounts of honey to see them through a rainy period or other sparse time in their single summer of existence. As we mentioned, the stingless bees store some honey, but not large amounts, since their colonies, though lasting longer than a single summer, are in the tropics where provision need not be made for winter.

Our honeybee, *A. mellifera,* however, has cleared a major hurdle in evolution—one that the lesser bees have not surmounted. *A. mellifera* is able to live in temperate climates where winter poses a major threat and to survive as a species, not through the tenuous means of single hibernating queens, as does the bumblebee, but in entire colonies, both workers and queens living throughout the winter. Furthermore these live, not in complete hibernation, but by maintaining within the hive a temperature elevated above the outside temperature to an extent that allows the bees to carry on bodily activities. The winter survival can be accomplished only by access to sufficient food, and this food supply the bees provide for themselves through the storage of large quantities of honey and of some pollen.

Man simply collects a portion of this honey supply for his own use, claiming it in his inimitable fashion as part of the bounty of the earth.

All honeybees belong to the genus *Apis,* there being four main species with subspecies or races of certain of these. The bee stock from which the genus *Apis* evolved probably originated in Asia, and three of the species are found in that area today.

The most primitive of the *Apis* is the species *dorsata,* known as the giant honeybee and found in the tropics of southern Asia. These bees build a single exposed wax comb, hanging it from trees or other such locations. The comb may attain the surprising size of 5 or 6 feet in length and may contain up to 40 pounds of honey within it. All cells within the comb are the same size, whether their purpose is to store honey or to rear brood of any of the three types—queens, drones, or workers. The bees also are large, being about twice as long as our familiar Western honeybees. The giant honeybees have the reputation of being pugnacious and reportedly have caused human fatalities through their concentrated attacks.

Although man has tried, he has not succeeded in "domesticating" *A. dorsata* as a source of honey, for the bees have the interesting but, to man, disconcerting habit of "absconding." That is, when conditions become unfavorable the entire colony simply migrates. Thus if insects such as ants threaten the colony, or if food supplies are short and the area cannot support the colony, or simply if food is more plentiful elsewhere, the whole group may move out. For this reason, these bees do not lend themselves to man's designs.

Apis florea is a second species of honeybee which also is confined to southern Asia. These are known as the little or dwarf honeybees, and certainly they are small when compared to their cousins the giant honeybees. The dwarf workers are only about ⅓ inch in length, with queens and drones slightly larger. These bees also build a single exposed comb, hanging it from branches. The length of this comb is measured, not in terms of feet as is that of the giant honeybees', but rather in inches, and the supply of stored honey is not measured in pounds, but in ounces. *A. florea,* however, is considered to be more advanced in some ways than *dorsata,* for *florea* constructs four distinct types of cells in its small comb—one type for honey storage, and one each for the rearing of queens, drones, and workers. This species, too, is known to abscond when conditions move it to do so. Being so small, and thereby storing so little honey, it is not of interest to man in the role of a producer of honey in quantity. Its honey, however, is reported to be prized by some people and collected for medicinal uses.

A. mellifera, we have noted, is known as the Western honeybee. It is also referred to as the domesticated honeybee and the true honeybee—all these names making it clear that we in our part of the world consider it *the* honeybee. This is the species to which we shall be referring in our discussion of life habits of honeybees. In southern Asia *mellifera* is not the common hive honeybee; there the so-called domesticated honeybee is *Apis indica.* This species is known as the Eastern honeybee and is very similar to *mellifera. A. mellifera* is found wild today in the Western world but is not found wild in southern Asia, as *indica* is; conversely *indica* is not found wild outside the East. Both *mellifera* and *indica* build multi-comb nests, usually in enclosed locations, both will live in hives provided by man, and both are important honey producers. The Eastern honeybee is, however, smaller than the Western.

Theoretically the ancestors of the Western honeybee developed in Asia; from this point they radiated outward in Eurasia and Africa. As natural land and water barriers arose through the ages, certain groups of *A. mellifera* developed in isolation from one another, resulting in different races of this species. These races vary somewhat in appearance, temperament, and habits. All will interbreed, and with man's increased mobility and ease of transportation, races of the Western honeybee have been increasingly moved about, experimented with, and interbred, until many hybrids and nonpure strains have developed. It is only in this regard that man has recently approached domesticating the honeybee to any extent, for by selective breeding of honeybees he is starting to change them to his designs. Honeybee queens can now be artificially inseminated to allow this selective breeding.

There were some barriers which Western honeybees or their ancestors were unable to breach. Thus *A. mellifera* did not make it on its own to Australia or to the Western Hemisphere. Europeans colonizing these two areas purposely brought honeybees with them. Eventually some of these hive bees escaped and so established a wild population. Some of the North American Indians were said to call these wild bees "English flies."

CHAPTER 10

The Honeybee Cycle

Among the social insects the honeybees have devised yet another position for their young—neither upside down, nor right side up, but on their sides. Each young honeybee, or larva, lies horizontally in its own individual waxen cell. The combs in which the honeybees rear their young and store their food are amazing pieces of production and engineering. They are built of wax secreted by members of the colony and are vertically hanging combs of double-faced sheets of hexagonal cells, the cells lying horizontally and opening to the sides. Each comb consists of a single center wall, which acts as a base for the cells built on either side of it. The combs are suspended from an upper support, being built from the top downward. A colony of honeybees will build numerous combs, and these hang parallel to one another.

Originally, and in the case of wild colonies today, these parallel hanging combs were built in hollow trees, in holes in rocks, or in similar locations. Man has, through the last few thousand years, provided *A. mellifera* with hollow logs, baskets, and other such accommodations to induce them to dwell therein and store honey for him. Today we have the modern hive which consists of a wooden box or a stack of several such interconnected boxes, each known as a super; this hive is equipped with a removable top. Within the hive are hung wooden frames in which the bees build their combs. The apiarist can open the hive from time to time to inspect the frames and, if he wishes, withdraw those that contain combs full of honey and replace them with new frames.

Among the honeybees the wax for the combs is produced by the workers only. It issues in the form of small scales from between the bee's abdominal segments and is produced only from the underside of the abdomen. As these wax scales appear they are removed from the surface of the abdomen, moved forward to the forelegs, and transferred to the mandibles. There the wax is manipulated and chewed; finally it is molded into place in the comb. Old wax is sometimes reworked and used again; additional materials, such as pollen, may be added in very small amounts.

The hexagonal design of the individual cells provides the greatest possible amount of storage space with the least possible amount of material (wax) involved in their construction. Each of the six walls of a cell acts also as a wall for an adjoining cell, thus no space is wasted between the cells at any point. One investigator found that 1 pound of wax was involved in the bees' construction of 35,000 cells. In this number of cells

Honeybees' waxen combs are built downward from an upper support. The individual cells open horizontally, and in certain of them the young are raised. In others, pollen and honey are stored. The wax and honey produced by the bees and the pollination of plants by bees have been and continue to be of great importance to man.

approximately 22 pounds of honey could be stored, or, of course, 35,000 young could be reared—the cells being equally important for food storage or for baby beds.

Three sizes of brood cells are built. Worker cells are the smallest, drone cells are slightly larger, and queen cells are quite different from the other two types, being large, peanut-shaped, and hung irregularly from the edges of the combs. Worker-size cells usually occupy the center portions of the brood comb, with drone-size cells being found nearer the periphery. Thus during the summer season within an active hive one would find brood comb, with the center containing young in their appropriate cells and in some cases at least the outer portions given over to food storage. Pollen is often stored in cells immediately surrounding the brood, and honey in the outermost cells of the comb. This honey and pollen surrounding the brood represents a nearby food supply for the worker bees to use in rearing the young. The bees do, however, store additional quantities of honey and so within a hive there are combs full of honey only, in back of, and sometimes above, the brood area. It is these combs that man can and does collect for his honey supplies, obtaining the honey without destroying any developing brood. Special-sized food-storage cells are not built. Pollen is usually stored in worker-size cells, and honey in the slightly larger drone-size cells. The honeybees are thus a degree less specialized in this regard than their "wild" relatives, the dwarf honeybees.

Brood rearing begins in late winter or very early spring and continues through the summer into late autumn. The single queen is the sole egg producer and at the height of the season she may lay more than her own weight in eggs every 24 hours, thus producing between 1000 and 2000 eggs per day! A healthy, active hive may include 80,000 adult bees. During the busy summer season the workers often work themselves to an early death, their average life span being only about 4 to 6 weeks. Therefore, the colony must continuously be replacing the work force with young healthy workers. A queen may often lay a total of 100,000 to 200,000 eggs each year to maintain a strong colony in prime condition. And a queen lives not merely a single year but usually continues this egg production for two to three years, and some as long as four or five years.

The queen wanders about on the comb in the brood area inspecting each cell as she comes to it. If her inspection reveals that a cell is empty and has been cleaned in preparation for the egg, she inserts her abdomen into the cell. Within a few seconds she withdraws it, having laid within the cell a single, long, slender egg. Then she continues on her way, repeating the inspecting and egg inserting. Here her duties end, and those of the foster mothers, the workers, begin, for the workers will care for the young from this point onward.

An egg hatches on the third to fourth day. The larva remains in its open cell, being fed progressively by the workers. Within approximately five days the worker larvae have completed this phase of their growth, and are ready to be sealed in their cells. This the workers do by capping the individual cells with wax. Inside the waxen covers each young bee spins a silken cocoon about itself for its pupal stage. The length of this stage varies with the sex and caste of bee. Queens are usually mature and emerge as adults approximately sixteen days after the egg was laid, workers in twenty-one days, and drones in about twenty-four days.

The care required by a single young is phenomenal. M. Lindauer, a foremost authority on honeybees, recorded the care given to a particular larva. He found that this involved 2,785 visits to the larva by workers from the time the egg was laid until the cell was capped. These visits took a total bee-working-time of 10 hours, 16 minutes, and 8 seconds. This, bear in mind, is for one larva—and the larvae present at any one time in the colony number well into the thousands. One investigator found approximately 38,000 cells containing brood in one colony. This included brood in all stages of development from egg through pupa. A thousand or more larvae may hatch in a single day, a like number may be emerging as adults at the same time, the queen may be producing approximately that many eggs on the same day, and perhaps a nearly equal number of adults will be dying of old age, accidents, or disease. As newly mature adults emerge from their cells, the workers clean and prepare these old beds for new eggs. And so the activities within the colony revolve in a busy circle from egg, to adult, to egg once again.

Lindauer's study showed that honeybee workers spent a total of 109 minutes and 37 seconds in actually feeding a single larva. This did not include the time spent in collecting and preparing the food for the actual feeding, which was considerable. In preparing to feed a larva, a worker inspects the larva in the cell, places her jaws close to the cell, and regurgitates a drop of liquid from her mouth. This drop of food may be placed on the floor or wall of the cell; it may simply be dropped onto the larva. The larva soon finds the offering and imbibes it. The feeding pattern is not one of direct transfer from mouth to mouth. Studies indicate that, unlike the social wasps, the larval honeybees do not produce any secretion for reciprocal feeding of the workers. The role of the secretion of even the larval wasps is open to some question, as we noted earlier. In any event, no such secretion is produced by the honeybee young, which are fed by the workers without any payment being demanded for services rendered.

For approximately the first three days of life, all honeybee larvae, regardless of their ultimate destiny—queen, worker, or drone—are fed a secretion produced by young worker bees. This is a product of the pharyngeal glands and is referred to as brood food, bee milk, or, when fed to queens, royal jelly. After the third day of life, however, the food given to larvae destined to be either workers or drones consists of this secretion diluted with honey and pollen, whereas the queen larvae continue to receive only the royal jelly. Queen larvae also receive food in abundance. Their cells are considerably more spacious than those of the workers', so there is sufficient space for an excess store of food with which the workers keep them supplied.

Drone honeybees develop from unfertilized eggs laid in drone cells by the queen, or occasionally by workers. Female honeybees develop from fertilized eggs. Whether a fertilized egg develops into a queen or a worker is a complicated matter not completely understood. Certainly both the quality and quantity of the diet given to the female larva has a vital role. The determining factor is not within the egg itself. This has been proved many times by transferring a larva less than three days old (which is approximately the time when differential feeding of the larvae begins) from a worker cell into a queen cell. The larva then receives from the workers caring for it the food accorded to a queen larva and ultimately it emerges as a queen, even though the egg from which it developed was laid in a worker cell. If the transfer takes place after the third day of larval life (after differential feeding has thus begun), it is not successful, the creature produced being either a worker or an intermediate form between worker and queen. Experimentally, young worker larvae were taken from their cells and fed on royal jelly which had been collected from queen cells and refrigerated until used. These did not develop into queens even on their abundant diet of royal jelly. However, when the experiments were repeated, using only fresh royal jelly taken from cells with larvae of approximately the same age as the experimental larvae, many of these subjects of the experiment developed into queens. It thus appears obvious that there is a substance within the royal jelly that promotes the production of queens and that this substance is easily lost or changed when the food is allowed to age for some time.

Young queen honeybees are normally raised in the spring and their purpose, of course, is to create new honeybee colonies. The new queens usually carry out this duty, however, not by leaving, but by staying at home. Among the honeybees it is the old queen who leaves home to pioneer, rather than her young daughters, although some of these may also leave. When conditions are propitious—and no one is quite positive just what all these conditions are—workers in a colony prepare queen brood cells. As mentioned earlier, these are completely unlike the usual hexagonal honeybee cells. The queen cells start as thimble-shaped hanging productions, the mouth opening downward, and are attached to the edges or bottoms of the combs. As the larva grows within, each cell is enlarged until it eventually takes on the aspect of a peanut. Only about a half dozen or so of these cells are built. The queen lays an egg in each and the resulting larvae are given both a particular diet and an excess of food, which, plus other determining factors in the food, cause the development of virgin honeybee queens.

About the time the first of these queen cells is capped by the workers, indicating that the young within has entered the pupal stage of development, a portion of the colony prepares to "swarm" or to set forth from the hive. The workers destined to leave home gorge themselves on honey. The old queen, whose egg production has fallen off with the advent of developing young queen bees, has slimmed down, not being distended with eggs, and is thus prepared to go traveling.

Some unknown signal or motivating force suddenly propels the honey-filled workers and the old queen forth from their hive, and this group of bees, which may contain up to almost half of the original colony, leaves its old home to establish a new one. The bees leading the swarm soon settle in some location, as on a branch, and are joined by the rest of the group. These thousands of individual bees alight one atop another and the group forms a cluster or seething ball of bees. The group may remain thus for a period varying from a few minutes to a few days. If it stays for any length of time, scout bees fly off individually to search for a proper home for the group. In some cases the scouts have begun their searching before the group has left its old home. Once the important choice of a new home has been made the swarm of bees moves off to establish itself in its new quarters. Occasionally a suitable location will not be found and the swarm will begin building combs in the open. Such colonies may endure for short periods but are never successful for long. Certainly they cannot endure a cold winter in such an exposed location.

Back in the original hive, the workers have been left without a queen, but with the promise of one or more developing in the queen cells. The first young queen to emerge is usually destined to become the new queen of the old colony. She searches out the other queen cells and she, or the workers, or both, destroy all the other young queens. Within a few days the young virgin queen flies out of the hive on her mating flight.

The marriage must be a first-class affair with a wedding flight—mating does not take place within the hive. The virgin queen may be accompanied from her hive by a swarm of workers and drones, and such a flight is known as a mating swarm. Or she may simply leave the hive alone. Queens may fly a mile or more from the hive at this time. The drones, it has recently been discovered, have special meeting places that are used each year, although each year by a new generation. The queen, on arrival at one of these meeting places, attracts the drones with a secretion of her mandibular glands. As she flies she is pursued by drones. One of these eventually overtakes her and they mate. The male's genital organs normally lie within his body, but when mating takes place these are rapidly everted, that is, forced outward, through muscular contraction. So firmly are portions of his genital system held in place in the queen's body during and following the mating that she can free herself from him only by ripping them from his body. The male quickly dies; it may be that he dies before his body is ripped apart, the process of eversion of his organs being fatal to him.

The queen returns to her hive, sometimes with the remains of the drone's reproductive organs still attached to her. These eventually fall away or are removed by the workers. This new queen now takes over the duties previously performed by her mother. In another year she will play the role of the old queen, and if all goes well will leave this hive in a swarm to found another colony, as did her mother before her.

In some cases a newly emerged queen is prevented by the workers from killing other developing queens in their cells, and these cell-bound queens are prevented, also by the workers, from leaving their cells for a few days. Thus the virgin queens are not allowed to encounter one another, for a confrontation would lead to a battle or battles between the queens. These battles would very likely result in death for all the queens except the single victor, and she, too, might be killed or so badly wounded as to be incapacitated. There is a plan involved in this retention of more than one virgin queen, but a plan worked out by whom and just how, we cannot say. Under this arrangement the newly emerged queen, either before or after her mating flight, will leave the hive with a swarm of workers, and this swarm will establish another colony, as did the old queen and her followers a few days earlier. In this way some colonies may produce two swarms, or sometimes even more, in one season. The first swarm, led by the old queen, is usually referred to as the "prime" swarm; the second and any later swarms led by young queens are known as "casts." By preventing the first virgin who emerged from killing the rest of the developing young queens, the workers have retained some of these in the colony. The virgins in excess of those needed to lead secondary swarms and to head the parent colony are finally killed, by the new queen, by the workers, or in battle, with one victorious virgin surviving to become queen of this parent colony.

If the queen of a colony becomes too old or otherwise unable to fulfill her duties, the workers will make preparations to rear a successor. This is normally done by preparing queen cells and raising a virgin who returns to the colony after her mating flight and takes over her mother's duties. Within the hive the new queen may meet her mother, the old queen, if this individual is yet living, and may kill her. In some cases, however, the two have been known to live together in the colony for some time, both laying eggs. If an old queen dies suddenly, with no provision previously made for a replacement, the workers may enlarge a normal cell containing an egg or a very young larva, remodeling it into an emergency queen cell and producing within it a virgin queen who will take over.

Bumblebees, many wasps, and most ants send forth new queens to face life and establish new colonies of the species on their own—sink or swim, no help given. Stingless bees send a portion of their workers and also part of their food supply out with a new queen to help her establish a colony. But the honeybees are unusual in that normally it is the old queen who leaves the nest to establish the new colony, taking with her a large group of workers from the old one. The new colony thereby has the advantage of a queen of proven fertility. It does face a number of challenges—finding a home, locating food supplies (since the only stock of food these bees have after leaving the home larders is the honey they carry in their crops), and then quickly building cells and rearing young as replacements for themselves. The worker bees who remain in the hive are also faced with a major hazard. Although they have food supplies and some developing brood, they are left without a fertile queen. There is developing queen brood, but should some misfortune occur, such as failure of the only surviving virgin to mate, this colony will face disaster. What determines—we wonder but cannot say—whether a particular bee, who certainly cannot think and come to a logical decision, will swarm and throw in her fortunes with the old queen, or remain in the hive and put her honey, so to speak, on the new queen?

CHAPTER 11

Honeybee Queens and Drones

When written history consisted simply of pictures on rocks, a Stone Age artist living in the area that is now Spain painted a scene showing an individual collecting honey from a colony of wild honeybees. Much later but still more than 2500 years before the birth of Christ, the Egyptians left a record in sculpture on a temple showing that they had "domesticated" honeybees—that is, they were keeping them and collecting their honey. For thousands of years man has had at least a gustatory interest in the bees' honey, and certainly he must have had at least a modicum of curiosity about the bees themselves. Yet not until the early part of the seventeenth century was it first suggested that the drones were males and that the "king," as the seeming ruler or important member of the colony, was actually a "queen." Even with these matters determined, almost two hundred more years passed before the general organization of the bee colony and the relationships between the queen, drones, and workers were to be reasonably well clarified.

Today it is obvious to us that the king is a queen and that she is of vital importance to the colony. We realize the significance of the drones, and we know a great deal about the activities of the workers. We are aware that each of the three types of individuals has its role to play in the colony, that all are vital, and that each type, for the purpose of carrying out its duties, varies greatly from the other two.

The drone has a single purpose in life—to mate with a young queen. Most honeybee drones must therefore lead lives of intense frustration, for a normal honeybee colony produces at most a mere three or four young queens and often only a single one. Since the colony and each of its neighboring colonies raise several hundred drones for each young queen they produce, and each queen mates only once, or at most a few times, the drone's chances of success at his life's calling are exceptionally slim.

The drone's body is highly specialized for the role he is expected to play. He is slightly larger in size than the workers. He has strong wings with which to overtake the flying queen. His senses—at least those which will aid him in locating a young queen—are more fully developed than are the workers' and queens'. His eyes are much larger: a drone has in excess of two and one-half times as many facets to his eyes as does a queen, and twice as many as does a worker. He has a highly developed sense of smell. The senses of both sight and smell are of major importance in detecting the presence of a young queen. The optic lobes of the drone's brain, the part having to do with sight, are large, correlating with the oversize eyes. The parts of his brain known as the mushroom bodies (groups of cells thought to be the higher centers for directing behavior) are noticeably small —smaller, in fact, than are these bodies in the brain of either a queen or a worker. The drone has brains for the job he is to do, but evidently he has few left over.

The digestive system of the drone is somewhat reduced in comparison with that of the workers. The drones are, however, fed by worker bees or simply help themselves to honey stores within the hive. They never forage for their food and lack many of the body hairs as well as the pollen baskets that are standard equipment on worker bees. These males work not at all. They have no stings. Drones fly out of the hives during good weather in their search for queens, and should their limited brain power fail to guide them back home, they will be allowed, providing the swarming season is at hand, to enter other hives and there will be cared for by the workers. This acceptance is accorded only to drones; foreign females are suspect and are often set upon and killed if they attempt to enter a hive other than their own.

Since it is for reproductive purposes that the drone exists, his reproductive system is highly specialized. A drone must be able to produce a supply of sperm that will last a queen for her lifetime of egg production, and he must be able to transfer this supply in a brief instant during the mating act. As a queen may lay 400,000 or more eggs in her lifetime and a very large percentage of these will be fertilized, each requiring a sperm, the drone's production of sperm is almost unbelievable.

If the drone achieves his objective and mates with a queen, he immediately dies, the act of mating killing him. If he does not mate he remains in the hive and is tolerated there until food supplies begin to dwindle or until autumn approaches. Under these conditions the workers neglect to feed the drones; they deny them access to the food supplies; they may even forcibly drag them out of the hive and prevent them from reentering; they may nip and bite them or even sting them to death. Even if the drones are simply forced out of the hive, they soon die of starvation. Regardless of the alternatives, it is an ignominious end for a once pampered sex.

The queen honeybee has become so specialized for her job that she can no longer lead an independent existence. She is incapable of foraging for her own food and she cannot found her colony unaided. Although she may be the mother of almost a half million children, she can neither house nor feed them, for her body secretes no wax with which to build cells, and she has no equipment for collecting pollen. Her senses of sight, touch, and smell are inferior to those in the workers and drones. The mushroom bodies in her brain are somewhat larger than the drones' but smaller than the workers'. Her digestive system is reduced in size. Evolution has prepared her to be an egg factory and as such her reproductive system has been emphasized; other systems have been de-emphasized as far as practicable. As an egg producer she ranks supreme. Early in the season as brood production begins, and again late in the season, the queen will produce several hundred eggs each day, and at the height of the season she may be producing 1500 or more eggs per day. In order that she may accomplish this feat the workers rather constantly stuff her with rich predigested food. Workers form a constant but changing retinue about her on the combs, gathering around, touching her, feeding her, and licking her body as she moves about laying eggs.

A queen usually mates only once, at the very beginning of her career. It is thought that occasionally she may mate more than once, and with more than one drone at this time, but the single mating is probably the normal procedure. Amazing as it is that the drone can produce sufficient sperm to last a queen her lifetime, it is equally amazing that a queen can store this quantity of sperm within her body and that it remains viable for the two to five years of her life.

During the mating act the drone injects his sperm deep into the female's reproductive system and the sperm make their way into the small hollow organ known as the spermatheca. Here in this special sac they are retained. The spermathecal duct opens from the spermatheca into the oviduct. As the queen produces an egg, and preparatory to its leaving her body, the egg passes down the oviduct. As it passes by the spermathecal duct, the muscular sphincter closing that duct is evidently relaxed, releasing one or more sperm. One of the sperm reaches the egg and enters it through a small opening at one end; further sperm are prevented from entering by an action that takes place within the egg. A single egg is fertilized by a single sperm. The egg thus fertilized will result in a worker or a queen, depending on the treatment accorded the larva developing from it.

For the queen to produce an egg that will ultimately develop into a drone, however, fertilization of the egg must be prevented. This poses a problem when we attempt to explain it. So minute is an individual sperm that we can scarcely imagine the queen's having enough control to release only a single sperm at a time. It would seem logical to suppose that excess sperm would remain in the oviduct after the passage of an egg and that these would automatically fertilize the next egg that followed along. However, the queen seems to be able to intersperse the laying of female and male eggs, depending on the types of cells she finds in her wandering about. Evidently her system, whatever it is, is completely or very nearly foolproof. Various theories have been proposed to explain this ability of hers. Possibly an egg passing down the oviduct carries with it to the outside all the sperm in the oviduct. Perhaps the sperm left in the oviduct retreat into the spermatheca before the passage of the next egg. Or, perhaps, through some stimulus the queen receives from the cell (which would be a drone cell), she is able to control the egg itself. Before the egg starts its passage through the oviduct, it may be changed in some manner so that a sperm cannot enter and fertilize it, although the egg may pass directly through sperm in the oviduct. Varied, little-known, and infinite are the many small worlds never seen about us. Within this very small living creature may be stored as many as a half million sperm, are produced a like number of eggs, and are incorporated the numerous behavior patterns that guide her in her activities and aid in assuring the continuation of her species.

CHAPTER 12

Honeybee Workers

The worker honeybee is the brains of the outfit, or so at least it appears when we observe her varied activities. The mushroom bodies of the worker's brain are larger than those of either the queen or the drones, and whereas drones and queens each have only one major activity in the colony, the workers are responsible for a variety of duties. During her lifetime each worker bee usually spends some time at all or at least at many of the jobs that must be done by the worker group in the colony. She does not learn one specific job and stick to it the rest of her life but rather is sufficiently versatile to carry out several activities. Her versatility is not wholly dependent upon her brain power, however. She is to a large extent ruled by her glands, but, conversely, the needs of the colony can to some extent exert an influence on these glands.

A worker's life is roughly divided into two parts. During the early portion of her adult life she is a house bee, carrying on duties inside the hive. During the latter part of her life she is a forager, spending most of her time outside the hive collecting food. If we could locate a model bee her life schedule would adhere to a plan similar to the following. For approximately the first three days of her adult life she would spend her time on the brood comb soliciting food from workers, resting, and cleaning out brood cells. From approximately the fourth through the eleventh day of her life she would feed on the honey and pollen stored in the nest, she would feed older larvae pollen and honey, and she would feed certain larvae on brood food. At about twelve days of age she would taper off on her brood-feeding duties and begin producing wax and join in building activities. She would start taking short flights out of the nest and would collect and store away food supplies delivered to the hive by foragers. After about the twenty-first day of her life she would become a forager, spending a great deal of her time outside the hive. After two to three weeks of foraging she would be expected to die of old age. It would no doubt be difficult to find such a model bee, but in general these are the duties performed by the workers—although many bees may not indulge in every one of them—and the development of the workers' bodies dictates to a certain extent that these activities will occur in somewhat this order.

The young worker cleans old brood cells by entering them head first, removing debris from them, and working over the inner walls with her jaws. She also spends time simply resting or moving about on the comb. This also is of benefit to the colony, for her presence aids in maintaining the higher temperature in the brood area that is important for the development of the young. She also spends time in begging for food, for the very young worker does not at first feed herself from the colony's stored food. Instead she solicits food from older workers and this she does by stretching out her tongue toward one of these individuals. When a worker is willing to comply with the solicitor's request, the donor regurgitates a drop of food which comes to rest on her tongue between her open jaws. The receiving bee places her tongue in the drop of food and imbibes it.

Beginning on about the fourth day of her life and continuing for approximately a week, the worker helps herself to honey and pollen stored in the nest. She concentrates particularly on eating quantities of pollen, which is a highly nutritious protein food. For the first few days that she is on this diet she often helps feed the older brood by giving pollen and honey to the worker larvae who are three or more days old. Two or three days of pollen consumption cause the worker's pharyngeal glands to develop. It is in these glands that the brood food, or bee milk, is produced. They consist of ducts with small bodies situated along their length. These ducts are located in the bee's head and open onto the back of the tongue, so that the material produced in them can be passed through the mouth to other bees or larvae within the colony. The bee milk is a nutritious food that is fed to all larvae for the first two to three days of life, to queen larvae throughout their development, and also to the queen in large quantities. The bees whose pharyngeal glands are well developed and who are using the bee milk produced in them to feed portions of the brood are often called the nurse bees.

Oftentimes, by about her twelfth day of life the worker's pharyngeal glands have begun to shrink and she is no longer producing quantities of bee milk. But at about this time her wax-producing glands have begun to secrete quantities of wax and so she now concentrates her efforts on secreting wax and building with it. Wax-secreting workers may hang in closely packed groups as wax is produced from glands on the underside of their abdomens. As the wax forms into scales, these are removed from the surface of the abdomen, worked, and molded into position where building activities are taking place. Wax-working bees also collect and rework old wax. In addition to building new combs, they repair old combs, cap cells, and carry out other duties involving the use of wax.

During this period in her life the worker begins to collect food supplies that are being brought into the nest by foragers. These older foraging bees bring a variety of substances back to the nest, the most important being nectar, pollen, and water. House bees will collect these materials from them, relieving the foragers to return to the field, while the house bees make the appropriate disposal of the materials. In this second to third week of her life the worker also begins to show an interest in the world outside her hive. She takes exploratory flights and in this way begins to learn the territory about the nest preparatory to becoming a forager.

Once a worker has made the transition from house bee to forager, her activities will be centered primarily outside the hive for the remainder of her life. These foraging activities and their most important product—the honey—are discussed in the next chapter.

Commonly in the early stages of the foraging activity, but at other stages also, some worker bees are diverted to guard duty, and they often combine this duty with foraging on a part-time basis. A guard bee appears to choose a "favorite" small area at the entrance to the hive. She stands alert, watching movements in the area. When a bee alights there the guard runs up and examines the newcomer with her antennae. If the bee is a member of the colony the guard quickly allows her to enter the hive. The newcomer's smell is her passport, for bees of each particular colony have a colony odor that identifies them as bees in good standing in that specific group. If the arriving bee lacks the proper odor and is therefore quickly identified as an intruder, there are various possible actions that the guard may take. She may proceed vigorously to maul the intruder, grabbing the stranger with her mouthparts and dragging her away from the hive. If the interloper is a robber bee, wasp, or similar enemy, it is identified at once and every effort is made to sting it to death immediately and without preliminaries. Where many hives are kept close together, foragers from one honeybee colony may by mistake enter a neighboring hive instead of their own home. If these foragers are laden with pollen or nectar and act in a dominant fashion—that is, simply act as though they belonged there and proceed to enter the hive, brushing off the guard as they go—they are usually allowed to pass unharmed and to enter the hive. However, if a strange bee not carrying food supplies mistakenly attempts to enter a hive and is challenged, she will often act in a submissive rather than a dominant manner. Her submissiveness is apparent to the guard, for the interloper makes no attempt to get away but appears to wait apprehensively for the worst and offers the guard a drop of food. The guard is not impressed by the offer but mauls the offender and drags her off. This submissive attitude does, however, appear to prevent the guard from becoming unduly upset and the intruder who acts in this way is often not stung and killed but simply towed away roughly.

As far as man is concerned, the honeybee's sting is one of her most famous characteristics. The sting rests inside a cavity at the tip of the bee's abdomen until needed, when it is protruded. It is connected to a poison sac containing the venom. The construction of the sting is such that, once the tip of it has penetrated the bee's adversary, the entire mechanism works itself deeper and deeper into the flesh in which it is imbedded, meanwhile pumping venom into the victim. There are barbs present on the extremity of the sting, and these prevent the bee from withdrawing its sting from man's soft flesh; the sting is ripped from the bee's body as she attempts to fly away, and she soon dies from the injury. However, a bee can remove her sting without damage after having used it on another bee or other insect, as an insect's chitinous covering does not hold the sting as does man's more elastic skin. A person stung by a bee feels a sharp pain at the site, later some swelling occurs, and there is itching and irritation. A very small percentage of people suffer a more severe reaction. A bee stung by another bee is not so fortunate, death being its fate.

The bees have long been noted for their industry and we think of the bee as busy because she usually is when we see her. But what of the times when we do not see her deep within the hive? Observations carried out by Lindauer followed an individual bee's activities both within and outside her hive. The study, covering observations lasting 177 hours, showed that this particular bee spent 56 of these hours simply moving about the hive inspecting the state of affairs, and almost 70 hours more loafing—this is the busy bee! Actually these easy hours serve a purpose. A resting bee within a hive aids in raising the temperature for brood rearing, and merely by being present in the hive she is part of a reserve force that can be called upon should an emergency or need arise in the colony.

The hours the worker spends patrolling are extremely important, for it is through this activity that each bee informs itself of the needs of the colony. Once these needs are known, the worker, in so far as it is possible for her to do so, attempts to fill them. Therefore, while each worker is somewhat limited in the things she can do, according to the state of development of her pharyngeal glands and wax glands, she can choose to do any one of several jobs at any one time. The choice she makes depends upon what she perceives as the most immediate need of the colony, and perhaps to some extent on her preference of jobs or the job she is most in the habit of doing. On this simple but extremely effective basis much of the work in a honeybee colony is organized. To a certain extent colony needs can even affect glandular activity in the workers. Experimentally a hive was stocked with a worker force composed only of older bees who were foragers. With brood to be fed, the younger of these workers fed on pollen and were able to regenerate their pharyngeal glands. Soon they were producing brood food and caring for the young. Conversely, an experimental colony with a worker force composed only of young bees soon had workers who ventured outside the hive and became the foragers for their colony long before they would ordinarily have done so in a normal colony.

Individual bees also vary greatly in the rate of development of their glands. For example, it is known that some bees have their pharyngeal glands and wax glands well developed at the same time and can therefore indulge in either brood rearing or building, or both. A worker with developed pharyngeal glands may not find sufficient brood to feed and so may turn to foraging at an earlier age than she would have normally. A house bee, regardless of her age, on finding a cell that needs cleaning may stop and clean it; it is not only the very young workers who indulge in this activity. One thing becomes clear—the workers do the jobs that need doing, and, most amazingly, they do not do them because they themselves benefit directly, but for the good of the colony.

"The bee from his industry in the summer eats honey all the winter," to quote a proverb. Is that all—or what exactly does the bee do during the cold, flowerless winter? We have been considering the worker bees and their activities during the summer months when comb building, brood rearing, food foraging, and honey making are the busy order of the day. With the coming of winter the bees' activities take on a different pattern.

The honeybees living in temperate climates are outstandingly different from wasps or bumblebees living in the same area, in that these latter insects have never developed the ability to maintain their entire colony through the winter months. Instead, all of their members die with the exception of the new queens, who themselves cannot remain active but enter hibernation. The honeybees, although cold-blooded—that is, having a temperature approximating that of the environment—can as a group maintain within a cluster of bees a temperature as much as 100° F. higher than that of the air outside the hive. This ability enables the entire colony to live through the winter. This affords the honeybees as a species many advantages: the queens are constantly protected and need never face colony founding or life on their own; the colonies are ongoing and the queen's lifespan may be several years rather than a single season; and when the season arrives for brood rearing and food gathering, a worker force is already present, so that a colony need not be started from bare beginnings each year.

As we discussed earlier, a young worker, a few days after she emerges from her cell, begins to feed on honey and particularly on pollen. As a consequence her pharyngeal glands develop. Her body also stores food reserves in organs known as fat bodies. During the summer months this bee normally would begin feeding the brood food produced by her glands to the young bees, and within a few days the food reserves in her body, including those that caused the development of the pharyngeal glands and those stored in the fat bodies, would be gradually drained away. She would probably then move on to wax production and finally to foraging, which is strenuous and dangerous work, and her life would soon come to an end. If a worker bee emerges from her cell in late summer or in the autumn, however, the amount of brood to be fed in the nest is greatly reduced below summer levels, the queen having tapered off her egg laying in preparation for winter. These autumn workers do not exhaust their body reserves in feeding brood, or in foraging, for foraging activities have also been greatly curtailed, since the colony has already gathered its food supplies for the winter. These workers therefore do not use up their body reserves in their efforts for the colony, and leading a relatively easy life they survive for several months. In contrast, a summer worker has a life expectancy of only about four to six weeks.

By the time cold weather approaches, a honeybee colony consists of the queen and her well-fed, rested group of "winter" workers. No virgin queens remain and the drones have long since been tossed out. If the colony has had a successful summer, the workers have cached away large stores of food to see them through the winter. With the onset of winter the temperature within the hive begins to fall. When it reaches approximately 57° F. the bees form a winter cluster. That is, the entire colony crowds together, forming a ball of bees. This ball is formed on the two sides of one or more combs within the nest. The queen is kept near the center and some of the bees in the very center will enter the cells, so that although the bees are on the two sides of a comb, only a thin layer of wax separates the two halves through the center. The bees feed on the stored honey in the comb, and the metabolism of their collective bodies and the random movement of legs, wings, and abdomens causes the temperature within the cluster to rise. The outer bees act as insulating layers, prevent the cold from creeping into the center, and prevent the heat generated by the bodies of the bees in the center from radiating out. The bees in the outer layers assuredly have an uncomfortable position, akin to the human trying to get warm at a campfire—it's hard to get both sides warm at the same time. In very cold weather these outer bees may become so chilled that they cannot move and drop away from the cluster and die of cold. It may be, although this is not definitely known, that the bees within the cluster rotate their positions, so that those in the outer layers move toward the center before they become immobilized, and the warm bees in the middle move out to take their turns in the cold.

When the air temperature is very low the cluster contracts, which helps to retain the heat; as the temperature rises the cluster expands, allowing some heat to be lost by radiation. To maintain life and to generate heat the bees must have sufficient food; therefore the bees slowly shift the position of the cluster on the combs from time to time, devouring the stored food as they go. Occasionally the environmental temperatures may be so low for such an extended period that the bees become too nearly immobilized to move to food supplies located nearby in the hive. In this case a colony may actually starve to death in the presence of nearby food, but such an occasion is rare. Normally, through digestion of food, muscular activity, regulation of the size of the cluster, and an excellent temperature sense, these bees, which individually cannot control their temperature to any great extent, work together to raise the temperature within the center of their cluster to a level that will sustain their lives.

Long before winter shows any indication of ending, the honeybees prepare for their spring activities by beginning brood rearing. As early as January or February the queen may start to lay eggs in order that additional workers will be available as soon as the first flowers come into bloom. A constant temperature of approximately 95° F. is required for the development of brood, and the workers provide this temperature within the brood area even when that of the environment is much lower. This they do by simply being present in the brood area in large numbers and giving off their body warmth, or when temperatures are too low for their mere presence to develop sufficient heat, they cluster over the developing brood, covering them with a bee blanket. In one study the temperature within a brood area varied only 0.7° C. in a 24-hour period, although the temperature in other parts of the hive varied 17° C. between minimum and maximum in the same period.

No less amazing than the honeybees' heating system is their cooling system. Since the brood needs a relatively constant temperature for development, the bees must also be able to prevent temperatures in the brood area from becoming too high in the summer when the outside temperatures rise. During this warm season a great deal of nectar is brought into the nest and water evaporates out of this nectar as it is becoming honey. This evaporation aids in cooling the nest. When temperatures begin to reach the danger point, worker bees within the hive will fan vigorously with their wings to induce air movement and cooling evaporation. If further measures are needed, water will be brought to the nest by foragers and this will be placed in and on cells where, through evaporation, it is of great value in reducing the temperature. Worker bees—sometimes thousands at a time—will even take drops of this water and spread it out in a thin film on their mouthparts, working it back and forth to provide additional evaporation. As each drop is evaporated the process is repeated. With hundreds or even thousands of bees providing water and like numbers aiding in its evaporation through fanning or proboscidal agitation, the temperature of the brood area can in most cases be kept below 100° F.

Someone erred on that proverb. The bee from *his* industry in the summer eats nothing all the winter, both from lack of industry and from being dead. But the bee from *her* industry—or at least from the industry of the previous summer's workers—does eat honey all the winter. None of the three types of bees can stand alone, and although the honeybee queens carry the lofty titles, and the drones are given preferential treatment and a life of ease, it is the common, ordinary worker bee who is indeed the brains, the moving force, and the strength of the honeybee colony.

CHAPTER 13

Flowers and Honey

A flower's purpose is not to attract or to be attractive to man, but to attract bees—or beetles, moths, butterflies, hummingbirds, and any other members of the animal kingdom that will aid in its pollination. The showy and/or odoriferous flower is an advertising gimmick, albeit a much more attractive and interesting one than those that man creates. A model or "perfect" flower is made up of many parts. In looking at such a flower we usually notice the showy petals, as these are its most outstanding feature. The petals as a group form the corolla. Just within the corolla are the male organs of the plant—the stamens which bear the anthers. Within the anthers develop grains of pollen. In the center of the flower are the female organs. The pistil, which is topped by the stigma, terminates in the ovary located in the base of the flower. Within the ovary are ovules, or immature seeds.

For the continuation of the species, these immature seeds must be fertilized. This takes place when a grain of pollen comes to rest on the stigma, sends a long tube down the pistil, and by reaching the ovary fertilizes the seed. Pollination, or the placement of the pollen on the stigma, is therefore of prime importance to seed-producing plants. Some plants are self-pollinated—that is, pollen from a flower can pollinate that same flower or another flower on the same plant. Many plants, however, must be cross-pollinated—pollen must come from another plant of the same species in order for fertilization to occur. Since plants cannot move about, those needing cross-pollination must depend upon wind or animals to bring them pollen from their neighbors. In this regard bees are of great importance to many plants.

Bees derive their entire food supply—pollen and nectar—from flowers. Of vital importance to the bees is the pollen the flowers produce, for this material represents the bee colony's entire protein supply. In collecting pollen for themselves the bees travel from one flower to another, and as they collect they also unknowingly distribute pollen. As a bee forages on a flower she often brushes against its stigma and leaves behind a bit of pollen which she has carried in the hairs on her body from another flower. She has thus delivered pollen from one plant to another, effecting pollination. She has taken quantities of pollen from the flower, but she has also given a little; and despite the difference in the two amounts, it is a fair trade.

Flowers often provide pollen in large quantities, and many of them also throw in an extra to improve the transaction. These flowers have nectar glands located within the flower, or sometimes elsewhere on the plant, which secrete a sugary liquid prized by bees. When a bee visits a flower to collect nectar, its body becomes dusted with pollen, just as it does when the bee is there for the purpose of collecting the pollen itself, and so once again the bee carries pollen on to the next flower, where a few grains of it will very likely come into contact with the flower's stigma and effect pollination. Many of today's flowers sport showy, colorful petals and send forth strong, appealing odors. Both declare the flower's presence to the hungry bee. Many flowers would not exist were it not for the service performed for them by the bees. Without the flowers, there would be no honeybees.

Foraging honeybees collect four main substances to take back to the hive. From flowers they collect nectar and pollen, from certain plants they gather a material called propolis, and from various sources they collect water.

Of these four materials the one least vital to the bees' well-being is the propolis. This is composed of natural resins and to these some wax may at times be added. This material, also known as bee glue, is used for altering the nest site. With it the bees may seal up cracks in the hive, reinforce the comb at certain points, decrease the size of the nest cavity, or cover and seal off offensive materials too large for the bees to remove. The resinous material collected for this purpose is carried to the hive in the pollen baskets on the bees' hind legs.

Water is collected by foragers when it is needed in the nest and is carried home in their crops and regurgitated within the hive. Water, we noted, can be very important in cooling the nest by evaporation when the colony is threatened with heat. It is also important in the bees' diet. When pure honey, rather than the more dilute nectar, is being used as the main food supply, the honey must often be diluted with water for feeding to the larvae. Water is also a necessary element in the diet of adult bees. Honeybees in collecting water are sometimes not the fastidious creatures we consider them to be. They collect water from many sources, sometimes being drawn to water supplies that have a smell attractive to bees, but not so to man, because of the variety of materials that we consider unpleasant dissolved in the water.

Certainly the model of misery would be a honeybee with hayfever, for pollen, the villainous agent causing this human suffering, is one of the two staffs of life for honeybees. They collect it on their bodies, store it in their homes, and eat it as a basic part of their diet. It provides them with a rich source of protein, vitamins, and fat, and thus, in conjunction with nectar, which is a carbohydrate, gives them a well-balanced diet. Some foragers tend to concentrate solely on pollen collection, others concentrate on nectar collection, while others occasionally collect both at the same time or switch from one to the other.

Honeybees, like bumblebees, carry pollen from the flowers back to the nest in special structures known as pollen baskets, or corbiculae. A bee setting out to collect pollen prepares herself by taking along a supply of honey in her stomach. Upon reaching the flower from which she will collect, she moves about on it, scraping off pollen with her mouthparts and legs, or biting the anthers to obtain their dustlike pollen. This pollen may then be moistened with some of the honey which the bee has brought along for this purpose. A bee's body is also covered with a plentiful supply of varied hairs and in these much loose pollen comes to rest. Pollen, of various colors depending on the species of plant, is sometimes white or red, but most often yellow; foraging bees often look as though they had been sprinkled with gold dust, so covered with pollen do their bodies become.

The bee arranges her pollen collection with remarkable speed, either while she rests on the flower or oftentimes as she flies on to another flower, or while she simply hovers in the air. Pollen that has collected on the mouthparts and on the hairs of the bee's face and forward portion of the thorax is scraped together by means of brushes of stiff hair located on the front legs. Brushes on the other two pairs of legs accomplish the same for adjacent parts of the body. Masses of pollen are collected from the brushes of the front legs by the middle-leg brushes, and these are then collected by the pollen combs on the inside of the hind legs. Finally, with these combs filled, one hind leg is rubbed downward against the other. On the downward stroke the moving leg scrapes off a portion of the pollen from the other leg. By use of special structures on the leg, this pollen mass is forced into the pollen basket on the outside of the leg which has made the downward movement. Succeeding collections push this first pollen mass and later ones higher into the pollen basket until it is filled.

A bee returning to the hive with filled pollen baskets will be carrying two large, slightly sticky, packed masses of pollen on her two hind legs. Inside the hive she will seek out a cell in which pollen is to be placed and with movements of her middle pair of legs dislodge the pollen masses on the hind legs, dropping the bundles into the cell. House bees will later pack the pollen down into the cell and more will be added to it by other returning foragers. Pollen is stored to be eaten by nurse bees and to be added to the larval bees' formula. Some of it is used soon after collection, some of it stored for future use. It is necessary for the bees to keep ample supplies on hand in order to have pollen available at all times, including late winter when brood rearing has started but flowers are not yet in bloom. The pollen that is to be stored for some time is often moistened slightly with honey and the cell capped with wax.

It is estimated that a bee colony will use at least 50 pounds of pollen a year and this is probably a minimum figure. To collect such an amount would require somewhere in the neighborhood of 2,000,000 foraging trips. In order to obtain a full pollen load on each of those trips, a worker may need to visit only one flower or as many as a hundred or more.

Poetically, nectar was the drink of the Greek gods; slightly more scientifically, it is the drink of the honeybees. The nectar produced by a plant in nectaries or glands within a flower, or in extrafloral nectaries located elsewhere on certain plants, is a liquid consisting primarily of various sugars dissolved in water with small amounts of other substances, such as aromatic materials. Many small living creatures partake of this sweet liquid, but certain animals, among them the bees and butterflies, are equipped with a long proboscis which enables them to obtain not only the easy-to-reach nectar but also the nectar from some flowers that produce it so deep within the flower that it is inaccessible to many insects.

A honeybee obtains nectar by means of her proboscis, and the drops are stored in her honey sac, or crop. After obtaining a full load of nectar she returns to the hive and regurgitates the nectar to one or often to several house bees. These workers receive it in their mouths and then process it. Often the forager will then return to the field to collect another load. Within the hive a worker who has received fresh nectar will go to a quiet part of the hive to carry out the work that will aid in changing the nectar to honey. Average nectar contains approximately 60 percent water. In order to prepare storable honey, much of this water must be eliminated, concentrating the sugars. The worker manipulates the nectar with her mouthparts to aid in the evaporation of the water. Partially unfolding and then refolding her proboscis, she repeatedly regurgitates drops of the nectar, exposing it through her mouth to the drying air. She may thus work the nectar for 15 to 20 minutes, and although water is being evaporated from it, certain digestive juices are added. This worked nectar will then be deposited in a honey-storage cell, where further natural evaporation of water will take place. The end product is honey, stored in neat containers sealed shut with wax lids by the bees.

A tremendous expenditure of effort is involved in making honey. While a bee may obtain a full load of nectar from one flower, much more often many flowers must be visited. Studies show some bees will at times need to visit 1000 blossoms to obtain a full load of nectar, and trips requiring even more visits have been recorded. Then consider that a full load of nectar for a bee is a very small amount of nectar indeed. Three or more bees will probably each spend a quarter of an hour or more manipulating this tiny amount of nectar before it is placed in the cells. And a good deal of nectar or honey must be consumed by other bees in order to produce the wax and build the cells for storing the honey.

Many wonderfully imaginative explanations have been proposed in the past to pinpoint the origin of honey, including the ideas that honey is the sweat of the sky or the saliva of the stars that has sojourned in the stomachs of the bees. No less imaginative are the uses that have been made of the honey itself and the wax which contained it.

For thousands of years honey has been considered simply as a delicious and nutritious food, especially prized because for many people it was one of the few sources of sweetening—sometimes the only source. It has been thought of as a medicine and used on wounds and inflammations. And if it did not cure the patient it often helped bury him, for honey will act as a preservative and, in addition to being used to preserve meat and leather, was sometimes used to embalm human remains, either for permanent burial or as a temporary measure until cremation could take place. Wine was made from honey, and mead, a fermented drink made from water and honey with malt or yeast, has brought intoxication to man through the ages. The Mayas celebrated with such a drink, descriptively called "fire-honey." Honey has been a beauty aid applied to the face and hands by fine ladies in many countries.

The wax of the bees has also been serving mankind for thousands of years. It too was used in medicine and in embalming. Wax gave and still gives light through candles, and on wax writing tablets the ancients recorded their knowledge. Wax has been important in sculpturing processes, used in cosmetics, and along with oil and earth was rubbed on the bodies of Roman wrestlers.

In addition to their products, the bees are of the greatest value in the pollination of crops. It is reported that 4000 years ago the Egyptians moved their beehives up and down the Nile on barges as a means of making nectar readily available to their bees. Today a large industry in this country is devoted to transporting bees and providing them for pollination where and when they are needed.

Honey estimated to be 3000 years old has been reported to have been found in an Egyptian tomb, and the figure of a bee was used on many Greek coins. In parts of the Far East fried bees were eaten and soup was made from boiled bee larvae, pupae, comb, and eggs. Poison honey, derived from flower nectar poisonous to man, has been used in warfare to incapacitate an enemy army. Long ago, when armies surrounded a city's walls, beehives were sometimes tossed into their ranks by the walls' defenders. And while not bees but rather their close relatives the hornets were used, the Viet Cong recently reported an "ingenious device" employed by their troops in battle. They posted an "army" of hornets on a besieged highway. The South Vietnamese troops unknowingly alarmed the "army," whereupon the human troops were forced to retreat. The results, according to Viet Cong sources, were eleven enemy soldiers injured and traffic blocked for hours!

CHAPTER 14

The Honeybees' Communication System

Scientists are notoriously conservative in accepting any scientific observation as fact until it has been well proven, and the more extreme the conclusion, the more proof they are likely to demand. Little wonder then that many of them tended to look askance at the conclusion reached in 1923 by an Austrian scientist named Karl von Frisch. His conclusion: that honeybees "danced" to communicate, and that in this act of communicating they relayed some very specific information. Over the past forty years Von Frisch's conclusions about the dance language of the bees have become generally accepted, although some important questioning of certain of these conclusions is currently taking place, as we shall note when we discuss the dance communication.

A foraging bee upon finding a good source of nectar near the hive fills her honey sac or crop and returns home. On the surface of one of the combs within the darkness of the hive she may then begin to "dance." In the subspecies of honeybee known as *Apis mellifera carnica,* we find that if the source of the nectar is within approximately 88 yards of the hive the bee will perform a "round dance." She turns in circles, alternately clockwise and counterclockwise, forming a figure of eight but with the two loops of the eight overlapping. As she dances amidst the mass of bees in the hive, her excitement excites some of them and they follow her actions, touching her with their antennae. Soon she stops and regurgitates to one or more of the other bees some of the nectar she has carried home. She may dance again, pause, and regurgitate more. By her dance she relays to the others the information that she is excited by her nectar find; by the odor on her body of the flowers from which she foraged and by the odor of the nectar she has given them, they are informed of the kind of flower on which she has foraged and for which they should search; by the form of the dance, the "round" form, they are advised that the source of the nectar is within approximately 80 meters of the hive; and from the vigor and duration of the dance they receive an indication of the value of the source, the better sources moving the messenger to dance more vigorously and at greater length. Some of the bees receiving her message will leave the hive, search for, and forage upon the nectar source she has described. If they too are excited by the source they will return to the hive, dance, and thus recruit additional foragers. The original forager will return to the source, and if the source continues to be of value, she may dance again when she returns to the hive with her load. The honeybees therefore have a fast and efficient method of directing the colony's efforts toward a valuable source of food. A forager returning with pollen will recruit in the same manner, the odor of the pollen she brings back, rather than a sample, being the clue that guides the other bees to the correct type of flower. As a source of nectar or pollen becomes exhausted or of decreased value, fewer and fewer returning foragers will dance, thus directing increasingly fewer foragers to it, and freeing the work force to follow the directions of other dancers to better sources of nectar or pollen.

If the crop to be exploited is farther away than 80 meters, the bees do a more intricate dance, which relays additional information. This is the "wag-tail," "tail-wagging," or "waggle" dance. In this the bee moves in a true figure eight, with the two loops of the eight separated by a straight line. In performing this maneuver the bee makes a straight run, executes a 360-degree turn to the left, again makes the straight run, turns 360 degrees to the right, and returns once again to the straight run. This figure is repeated numerous times. During the straight portion of this dance she "wags" her abdomen from side to side—hence the name for the dance. In the waggle dance she provides the bees following her with two pieces of information not given in a round dance. She relays rather specifically the distance of the food source from the hive, and she also specifically relates the direction in which it lies; in contrast, the round dance only states that the source is within a circle with an 80-meter radius of the hive.

Scientists are not positive exactly which signal in the dance serves as the indicator of distance. It may be the length of time it takes the dancer to complete one full circuit of the figure eight, or the number of waggle runs in a period of time, or the duration of waggling in each run, or the number of waggling movements in each run. Man finds it easiest to interpret if he measures the bees' description of distance in terms of the duration of a complete circuit of the figure eight. If the source is nearby, more circuits are completed than if it is at a greater distance. The farther away the source, the fewer circuits completed in a period.

Experiments have shown that the bee measures distance not in terms of actual distance but in terms of the effort involved in reaching the goal. For example, if the bee must fly against the wind, a longer distance is indicated than if there were no wind. If a bee has a tail wind to help her, the distance shown in the dance is less than would normally be given for the same trip. A bee forced to fly uphill reports a longer distance in her dance than is reported for the same distance traveled on a flat plane. The information that is given is primarily for the outgoing trip; a head wind slowing the bee down on the outward trip would of course become a tail wind on the return trip, with an opposite effect in energy expended.

It is the straight, tail-wagging portion of the dance that indicates the direction in which the food source lies. A returning forager may at times alight outside the entrance to the hive on the alighting board and perform the wagging dance there on a horizontal surface. In this instance she will, in the straight tail-wagging portion of the dance, point in the exact direction in which the food source lies. This she is able to do by having memorized the angle of her flight in relation to the sun on her trip to the flowers. Normally, however, the returning bee dances within the dark hive on the vertical combs, rather than on a sunlit horizontal surface. In this case she cannot in her dance point toward the food crop. Therefore, a most remarkable adaptation takes place. The angle existing between the direction of the sun and the feeding area is changed into the same angle related to gravity. Thus if a bee wishes to show in her dance that foragers should travel directly toward the sun, the straight, tail-wagging portion of the dance is made vertically upward on the comb. If the forager should fly directly away from the sun, the run is made straight down on the comb. If the food source lies 40 degrees to the right of the sun, the straight run of the dance will point 40 degrees to the right of the vertical on the comb. If the source is 80 degrees to the left of the sun, the run will point at an angle 80 degrees to the left of the vertical. The dancing bee, using the sun as a reference point, remembers the angle to the sun at which she traveled horizontally on her outward journey, relates this angle to gravity, now using gravity rather than the sun as her reference point, and communicates knowledge of this angle on a vertical plane. The bees receiving the information must then transpose this knowledge back to a horizontal plane as they fly out of the nest following the directions they have been given.

If a bee cannot reach her destination by following the most direct route —a beeline—but must fly along two sides of a mountain rather than over it, the message will relay directions for a straight beeline approach. The bee is thus dancing an angle that she never actually flew. However, this information, combined with the distance information that she also relays, will lead her nest mates to the goal.

It has been discovered only recently that sounds are often produced by the dancing bee during the waggle run. The source of the sound is the flight muscles in the thorax; the sounds are probably received as vibrations, and the honeybees' antennae are apparently sensitive to these vibrations. These sounds are added to the dance when the food source being described is of good quality but may be absent if the source is not a particularly good one. Dr. A. M. Wenner has suggested, as a result of his studies on honeybee sound production, that the sounds produced during the straight-run portion of a honeybee's waggle dance—either the length of sound production or the number of sound pulses—may communicate to the bee's audience the distance from the hive to the food source she is advertising. Further research in this field should prove exceedingly interesting.

Another recent discovery is that the bees localize their dancing sites within the hive according to the distance of the foraging site from the hive. Sites far away from the hive are described deeper in the hive than are closer sites.

So accurately do the bees, through their dancing, describe foraging or possible future nesting sites for swarms setting forth from the old colony that scientists have deciphered the code, followed the directions, and arrived at the correct sites. M. Lindauer has three times interpreted the dances describing possible nesting sites and each time was able to arrive at the nesting location prior to the subsequent arrival of the swarm!

Although man can often decipher at least a part of the bees' dance, thus seemingly supporting Von Frisch's conclusions, Dr. Wenner has recently questioned some of Von Frisch's and other workers' conclusions in some areas of dance communication. Experiments carried on by Dr. Wenner and his associates lead them to suggest that the importance of the waggle dance to the bees may have been overrated. They suggest that while the dance may contain distance information, the bees may not use this particular information. Instead they may be using the odors of hive mates or other bees, food odors, or other cues at the actual feeding site to determine their final destination, rather than the distance information received through the dance in the hive.

We have noted that a bee orients herself through the position of the sun. However, she does not have to see the sun directly in order to determine its location, orient herself, and describe foraging locations later to her nest mates. A bee's eyes can detect polarized light, an ability shared by numerous other creatures but not by man. Light reflected from the blue sky is partially polarized—that is, the light waves vibrate on one plane, in contrast to ordinary light in which the light waves vibrate in all planes. The polarization pattern from the blue sky is correlated with the position of the sun. Thus distinctive light patterns originate from different parts of the sky at different times of day. Therefore, if a bee can see only one small bit of blue sky, the polarized light pattern from it will inform her of the location of the sun, and she thereby orients herself.

Bees can even find their way when the sky is completely overcast, with neither sun nor any blue sky in sight, for the eye of the bee is also sensitive to ultraviolet rays of light. When the sun is covered by clouds a slightly higher percentage of ultraviolet light penetrates through the clouds directly in front of the sun. The bees' perception of ultraviolet light is sufficient to recognize this slight difference and to orient themselves by it.

The sun is the bees' reference point or compass from which directions are taken, but the sun does present them with certain difficulties. The position of the sun in relation to the bees is constantly changing; the sun disappears at night, shifts during the day, varies in location at different seasons of the year. Thus the sun is not a constant reference point, but the bees are able to take this into consideration. If a bee communicates the location of a food source by dancing at a certain time of day and then continues working the source and dancing her find, the direction she describes to the other bees by the angle of her straight, wagging run will shift as time passes. The directions she presented in the first dance will not properly describe the location of the same food source an hour later, for the sun's position, the reference point, will have moved a certain number of degrees. The angle of direction given in the dance must therefore be changed by the number of degrees the sun has moved, and this the bee does. She can memorize the new angle on each outgoing trip, but when swarming takes place, her ability extends even further.

As a group of bees prepares to swarm, or after one has left the hive but has not chosen a permanent location for its home, scout bees will explore the surrounding terrain in search of suitable quarters. Upon finding a possible location they will return to the hive or to the swarm and dance their finds in the same way that bees relate the location of a source of food. A honeybee returning to the hive and communicating the location of a food source will dance for a short time and then return to the field, but a bee advertising a nesting location in a hive may continue her dancing over a long period. She has no reason to leave the hive immediately, and being sold on her choice of location she dances for extended periods to emphasize the value of her find. Such a scout-turned-dancer changes her dance with the passing of time, constantly relaying to her audience the correct directions to her find for the given moment. Although she may dance for several hours in the darkness without seeing the sun or blue sky, she is able to take into account the passage of the sun and adjust her directions accordingly. This would not be possible if bees had no perception of time, and it has been found experimentally that bees do have an inner time clock or time sense that enables them to perceive the passage of time.

The rhythm of the wagging dance also requires a time sense, for the speed at which the dance is executed declares the distance to the goal. The differences in speed with which a complete figure-eight cycle to designate various distances is made may sometimes amount to only 0.05 second. The bees receiving the information must in turn be able to detect these very slight differences in speed and to use the knowledge in terms of distance to be traveled.

In regard to this time sense, bees can be trained to come to a feeding station at certain times of the day, if food is made available there only at these particular times. This occurs very naturally also, because the nectar of many flowers flows only at certain times of the day, or the flow is much heavier during a particular part of the day. Bees display a flower constancy —that is, once they have begun foraging on a certain type of flower, they often continue to work only that one crop as long as it is worthwhile. And just as your cat always shows up at its appointed feeding time, foraging bees quickly learn the time or times of day that optimum nectar flow occurs in the plants that they are working and forage on them only during these particular times. The remainder of the 24 hours they tend to spend resting in the hive. The time sense is thus also of value in a foraging economy. But whereas your cat regularly comes begging for its dinner at a certain time, not only because it is accustomed to being fed at that time but also because it is hungry, hunger would not be expected to be the motivating force in sending the bee out to collect, since she has stored food available to her in the hive at all times. Her motivation is probably something else that is related to her social way of life.

The bees' time perception is tied to the 24-hour day-night cycle. Bees can be trained to come to a feeding dish several times a day if food is presented at these particular times; they can be trained to collect at two different locations each day if food is presented at a different time in each location; and they learn to appear at the feeding station only when especially concentrated sugar syrup is available if the syrup presented at different set times each day is of various concentrations. Experiments attempting to train bees to a 19-hour or 48-hour cycle or other such "unnatural" day, are unsuccessful.

Experiments carried out with bees in closed rooms in which light and temperature were kept constant showed that the bees would appear at the feeding dish at 24-hour intervals as trained, although they were not able to see the sun or blue sky as an aid to determining the time of day. To test whether these bees were dependent upon some other external stimulus in the environment for their time sense, or whether this time sense was truly an internal thing, bees were trained to come to a feeding dish at a particular time of day while being kept in a room where temperature and light were constant. They were then transported by air from Paris, where the training had taken place, to New York and there placed in a similar temperature- and light-constant environment. Although a 5-hour time difference thus occurred in their environment, the bees again foraged exactly 24 hours from the last time they had foraged, showing that they were ruled by an internal time sense which was functioning without reference to sun, polarized light, or other external stimuli.

A similar experiment was carried out later, but in this case the bees were not kept in a light-constant environment. Bees trained out of doors on the east coast of the United States were flown to the west coast. If only an internal time sense were involved, these bees would be expected to forage in the west 24 hours after their last foraging on the east coast. The first day in the west there was foraging activity 24 hours later, as expected, but there was also a rise in foraging activity at the 25½-hour point. The second day the bees were also active at these two major periods, but each period took place 1½ hours later than on the previous day. On the third day after displacement, the first foraging activity remained constant at the point it had reached the day before—that is, 1½ hours later than the point where the 24-hour interval would have fallen; the second peak of activity occurred ½ hour later than on the previous day. This second period of activity thus shifted to a time 3½ hours later than it would have been had the exact 24-hour time interval been sustained, and 3½ hours is the approximate time difference between the east and west coasts. The first peak of activity, however, continued to fall just 1½ hours past the 24-hour point. The conclusions reached from this were that the bees use two systems for time measurement—an endogenous system, tied to a 24-hour rhythm, and an exogenous system—and that each can influence the other to a certain extent.

The time sense of the bee then is tied to a 24-hour cycle. It is to a large extent internal but may be affected within limits by external stimuli. It aids the bee to forage under optimum conditions, makes possible the use of the shifting sun as a reference point for way-finding, and is a necessary factor in relaying distance to other bees in the waggle dance, and for their understanding of this.

In an effort to understand how the "language" of the honeybees evolved, inquiry has been directed into many areas, one of which has been the exploration of the language of other species of *Apis.*

All *Apis* species have been found to use both round and wagging dances to convey information. *Apis florea,* the dwarf honeybee, however, dances only on a horizontal surface, using the top of the open comb for her dance platform. Here she is able to give directions that point directly toward the goal she wishes to indicate and need not transpose her message for presentation on a vertical surface. *A. florea* is therefore considered the most primitive species of *Apis* in its ability to communicate.

A. indica, the Eastern honeybee, communicates in the same general manner as *A. mellifera,* dancing on the vertical comb in relation to gravity. *A. dorsata,* the giant honeybee, also dances on the vertical comb, but this is built in the open air. This bee is thought to be less advanced in her communication system than *mellifera* or *indica,* although more advanced than *florea. A. dorsata* appears to require a view of some portion of the sky as she dances, in order to give her directions properly.

When investigations of the dances were carried out on the various races or subspecies of *Apis mellifera,* it was found that, just as each race had developed certain small physical characteristics that differentiated it from the others, so too their "language" had varied. Basically the language of all honeybees is very similar—round and wagging dances being used by all species—but certain minor variations or dialects had developed among the races.

We stated earlier that at certain distances from the food source the bees change from a round dance to a wagging dance. This transition does not always take place at a certain definite point but may vary slightly for the race and is highly variable between races. For example, *A. mellifera carnica,* which we have been using for an example, may change from the round dance to the wagging dance when the goal described lies anywhere from 50 to 100 meters from the hive, though approximately 80 meters is the more normal point. The changing point for *A. mellifera intermissa* is 60 meters; for *A. mellifera ligustica* 30 meters; and for *A. mellifera fasciata* 10 meters. All races except *A. mellifera carnica* have developed a dance intermediate between the round and wagging dances; this modification is called the sickle dance. In the sickle dance direction is given by the bisector of the two loops of the dance.

Moving to other species of *Apis,* we find that the Asiatic honeybees show a great difference from the various races of *A. mellifera. A. indica* is reported as changing to the wagging dance when the goal is only 2 meters from the hive; *A. dorsata* starts the wagging dance at 3 meters; and *A. florea* at 5 meters.

The dance rhythms performed by different species of *Apis* and by different races of *A. mellifera* also vary between them. Thus to bees of one race a certain number of dance patterns completed within a given time in a tail-wagging dance evidently indicates a certain distance. That same distance may be represented by a slightly different number of completed patterns by another race or species of honeybee. The codes used to indicate distance thus vary among the "dialects."

Experimentally, bees of one race have been placed in the hive of another race, after precautions were taken so that the strangers would be acceptable to their hosts. Just as with a human tourist asking directions from an inhabitant of a foreign country, when neither understands the other's language very well, misunderstanding resulted. Bees danced directions according to the code of their race, bees of the other race interpreted the directions according to the code of their own race, and vice versa. Following the directions as she interpreted them, a bee might go either too far in her search for food or not far enough, but another time, if she was fortunate enough to "listen" to a member of her own race, she might find the food precisely where she thought it should be.

One wonders if honeybees could become psychotic. Under an artificial situation such as this, might not a honeybee begin to wonder if she really was losing her grip?

CHAPTER 15

Honeybees' Abilities

Mexicans are well known for their love of bright colors and they extend their use of colors to their beehives. A Mexican apiary will contain an array of hives in various shades of pink, green, red, yellow, blue, and other bright colors. This is not done simply as a decorative measure but to aid the bees in recognizing their own particular hive. This hive painting is also done to some extent in other countries. Basically the idea is correct, since bees are color conscious, but the human hive-painter often fails to take into consideration the fact that the color range seen by bees is not exactly the same as that seen by man.

Bees see four main colors—yellow, blue-green, blue, and ultraviolet. Orange, yellow, and green probably appear the same to the bee; blue, purple, and violet appear alike; the bee cannot see red, it being the same as black in her sight. However, bees can see ultraviolet light as a color, which man cannot.

Man sees the color white when all the combined rays of the visible spectrum are reflected to his eye. The same is true for bees—that is, in order for a bee to see the color white, all the colors that the bees are capable of seeing must be present, and these include ultraviolet. Many flowers that appear white to man absorb ultraviolet light rather than reflecting it. To man, unable to detect either the presence or the absence of ultraviolet light, this makes no difference to the white color he sees. To the bee, however, it makes a vast difference, and she sees those of our "white" flowers that absorb the ultraviolet light as a complementary color of ultraviolet, which is probably blue-green. If a beekeeper wishes to aid his bees by painting his hives, he is well advised to forget the rainbow effect and to concentrate on using the colors that present the greatest contrast to the bees' eyes: blue, yellow, black, and a white that absorbs ultraviolet and thus produces for the bees' eyes a blue-green color.

Bees, as successful foragers, are dependent upon a number of their highly developed senses, eyesight and the recognition of some colors being among these. This recognition of colors is very important to the foraging honeybee, for flowers that are brightly colored (to the bee) attract her attention, their color helping her to locate them as food sources more easily. Also, remembering the color of the crop on which she has been working no doubt helps the bee to remain constant to a particular kind of flower as long as it is profitable for her to do so.

The bees' sense of smell is also of great value to them in their foraging activity. Bees have a more acute sense of smell than does man; that is, bees are able to detect lower concentrations of certain odors than can man. Experimentally, bees have learned to distinguish more than forty odors. Their olfactory organs are located in the antennae, and since the antennae are mobile and extend in front of the bee's body, they can be brought into very close contact with the substance producing the odor. For example, the antennae can actually touch a flower, move over its various parts, probe into its center. Man, on the other hand, detects odors through nerve endings deep in his nasal cavity. By placing his awkward nose near a flower he can detect the odor of the whole but not those of the individual parts of the flower, if these vary as they do in some flowers. The bee can detect the odors of the various parts. Von Frisch in his work with the bees determined that in some flowers there are nectar guides, consisting of special colors or odors to guide the bees to the nectar sources within the flower. Thus some flowers have what Von Frisch refers to as scented sap spots, which through their stronger or different odors guide the bee to the nectar source; other flowers simply present a greater intensity of their odor nearer the base or center of the flower. The foraging bee can take advantage of these odor signposts because her antennae can search about the flower and register the variations in quality or quantity of odor.

The nectar guides may consist of special color areas on the flower in addition to, or in place of, the odor guides. The color of the flower surrounding the area in which the nectar is located may be a different shade of the same color as the remainder of the flower or may actually be a different, contrasting color. Because of the differences between's man's color sense and that of the bees, such guides are sometimes obvious to bees but not to man—for example, when ultraviolet is concerned.

The ability of bees to distinguish many different odors and to associate a particular odor with the crop on which they are working at the moment helps them to return time and again to the same crop and to maintain their flower constancy. This ability to distinguish odors is also of vital importance in determining from dancing bees the food source the dancers are advertising. The messenger bee cannot relate the color of the flowers to which she is referring, but she does relay the facts of distance, direction, odor, and to some extent quality by the vigor of her dances and perhaps through sound production. The information about the odor of her find is included on her body, which carries the scent of the crop, and in the nectar or pollen samples she passes out to her audience. The advertised odor of the crop helps the new forager to find the crop for the first time. The bees are sometimes guided to the exact blossoms on which the dancing bee foraged, as she may mark these with a scent produced by the Nassanoff gland, which is a scent or odor gland on the bee's abdomen. An odorless source of food, such as a dish of syrup used in an experiment, may also be thus marked, helping the bees that follow to locate it.

The knowledge of the crop's odor and color that the bee acquires on her first visit helps her to return to that crop time and again, until she finds a better crop on her own or is persuaded to change crops by other bees. Aided by knowledge of the crop's color and odor, the bee displays a crop constancy which is important in the pollination of plants, because it helps to insure that a plant will be brought pollen from another of the same species, rather than pollen from a plant of a different species, which would be worthless. Flower constancy is of value to the bees also, for once a bee has learned to work a certain crop in a certain general location, it is easier for her to continue this pattern than to be constantly searching for food sources.

Once a bee has located a source of nectar she must taste the nectar to determine whether it is of sufficient value to be collected. A bee can taste not only with her mouthparts but also with her antennae and her feet! Bees are capable of distinguishing four distinct tastes: sweet, sour, bitter, and salty. Their taste sense differs from man's to a great extent; many substances that are sweet to man do not appear to be so to bees, an example being saccharine. The bee is less sensitive to some bitter substances than is man, but more sensitive to salt and sour tastes. Nectar, in order to be of real value to the bees for honey production, must contain a high concentration of sugar, and many flowers produce nectar containing a sugar content of 40 percent or higher. If better supplies are not available, a bee may collect nectar with a sugar concentration as low as 5 percent, for immediate food sources rather than for storage; but if the nectar contains less than 30 to 40 percent sugar, the energy expended by the bees in manipulating it and evaporating the water from it for honey production would be greater than the energy to be derived from the end product. Thus foraging bees taste the nectar, and unless the sugar concentration is up to a certain level, or unless their need is great, they do not collect it.

It has been found by experiments that a bee learns the details of a food source only as she approaches it—she observes and records its color, odor, shape, and immediate environment. As she leaves the source, she often flies about it and at this time learns its location in relation to more distant objects or landmarks. Thus a bee is not only guided by the sun or by polarized light but also uses landmarks and actually learns the foraging area. Distinctive landmarks, especially those that point in a straight line from the hive to the food source, are evidently often used when available. Such a landmark might be a hedge or road. The bees may learn these and where they are applicable use them to the exclusion of other means of guidance. In other words, they are probably taking the easy way. In an experiment bees were trained to feed at a dish a certain distance south of their hive and were aided in their orientation by a forest edge running north and south in that area. The bees were then moved to a new location that also had a forest edge, but this time running east and west. Upon their release from the hive the foragers, following what they discerned as a familiar forest line, flew west, obviously following the landmark, instead of flying south to the feeding dish as they would have done had they been following directions derived by sun navigation.

Bees are not born knowing the area about their hive but must learn it, and landmarks are of value in this. A bee before beginning her foraging duties will take orientation flights about the hive. She ventures out of the safety of the hive and flies about it, gradually extending her flights to greater distances. During this time she is learning the location of the hive and the area around it in relation to the distinctive landmarks. When a bee returns to the hive after a flight, these landmarks help her to find its general location, and, as when she is closing in on a flower target, no doubt the color of the hive, and particularly its odor, help her to pinpoint its location.

Man has invented a good word for explaining the unexplainable—

instinct. Instinct does have a valid meaning in connection with the hereditary factors in behavior, but the term has been something of a catch-all, concealing lack of knowledge concerning animal behavior. Scientists are increasingly learning about the causes of certain behavior and have removed a good deal of cloudy conjecture about instincts. Whereas at one time it was thought that creatures such as the insects must be almost entirely ruled by instincts—that is, inborn behavior patterns—it is being found that this is certainly not entirely true. Many of the honeybees' actions are instinctive, as are certain actions of all creatures, including man, but the honeybee is capable of learning and her behavior is altered because of this learning. Learning the landmarks about a hive or food source is but one example.

Interesting experimental work in recent years has shown that bees even learn, rather than having been born with, the knowledge of the sun's path in the sky. Lindauer determined that bees' ability to orient themselves by means of the sun and to relate this orientation in the wagging dance was innate; they were born with this ability. However, a knowledge of the daily course of the sun was not innate; each bee had to learn it. By experiments he determined that approximately 500 collecting trips on the part of the bees were required for them fully to learn the ecliptic, or apparent path of the sun. In an interesting experiment bees were raised completely away from sunlight, then allowed to forage in sunlight only in the afternoons for thirty-five days. They had therefore never seen the sun during the morning hours. Yet when they were at last released during the morning they were able, by using the morning sun, to find the feeding point to which they had previously been trained when they had used the afternoon sun. They were thus evidently able to extrapolate from their limited knowledge of the sun's path, and to apply this extension of knowledge successfully.

With her tiny brain then, a bee can learn and subsequently profit by her learning. And, just as with man, who has a brain considerably larger, the bee world evidently has its slow learners, its fast learners, its eccentrics, its pioneers, and its steady, dependable core.

That slow and fast learners are present is evident when bees are experimentally tested in mazes. Some learn the way quickly, others more slowly, and some never do learn. The dependable core consists of the majority of bees who carry on the jobs in the hive and those foragers who upon finding a good food crop become constant in their collecting as long as it remains of value. These bees often collect from their crops only at a certain time of day, as when the nectar flow is greatest. The remainder of the time they rest within the hive and are not tempted to follow directions to other crops when these are advertised by other bees. When bees dance in the hive to announce that the flowers on which an idle bee has become accustomed to working are once again producing, the idlers become interested and return to the field. When a forager finds her crop deteriorating, she may search about for a better one and ultimately change crops if she finds one superior to what she has been working; she may, however, continue to check on her old crop from time to time, and if conditions there improve may switch back to it.

Some bees, however, tend to be scouts and leave the hive evidently simply to search for good crops. If successful they will advertise their finds and turn collectors. There seem to be relatively few scouts or pioneers in a hive; most of the bees tend to be followers, working steadily once they have been given directions but not often taking the initiative themselves. This, too, is a case not unknown to man.

CHAPTER 16

Organization of the Honeybee Colony

Seventy thousand or more honeybees can live together in harmony, work for the good of the group rather than each for herself, defend the colony, reach a democratic agreement on a home site, and prepare for the future by storing food. How is such an organization possible? A great deal of it depends, surprisingly, on tastes and smells.

Bees are constantly transferring food in the colony. Young larvae are fed on brood food produced by glands in the nurse bees. Queens are also given this secretion. Older larvae are given some of this milk, plus honey and pollen. Foragers regurgitate to house bees nectar they have collected and brought back in their crops; house bees transfer food from one to another. Lacking pots, pans, and serving spoons, adult bees use their crops and their mouths for the purpose of transferring food. There is thus a constant circulation of food supplies in a bee colony, and these food samples act as a sort of colony communication system. Certainly a bee who receives a nectar sample from a dancing returning forager has had communicated to her directly information as to the type of flower that has been visited. This food transfer also passes pheromones, which are chemical signals, about the colony. Such a sharing of food also insures that the workers will all receive a similar diet and that through their metabolism of this diet they will come to have the same body odors. Foraging activity between even nearby hives usually varies enough—that is, a different percentage of workers from each hive forages on various crops—so that the odor of no one colony is exactly identical with that of any of its neighbors. However, hives have been placed experimentally in an area where only one food plant was available, and after a period of two months the members of the hives came to have such similar colony odors that the bees were unable to distinguish their hive mates from those bees that were simply neighbors.

A portion of the colony odor is absorbed by the bees' bodies simply from their being among their companions in the hive. Bees from one colony can be introduced successfully into another colony, provided that they are first placed in their new hive in such a manner that they are protected, as in a screened container, but so that their bodies can absorb the odors about them; this eventually makes them acceptable to the colony members. Man may thus introduce a new queen into a colony after first removing the old queen.

The Nassanoff gland on the abdomen also contributes to the world of odors in which the bees live, forming a constituent of the colony odor. As has been mentioned, foragers mark special food sources with the scent of this gland, and often workers may be seen in front of the hive with the scent gland exposed and the wings fanning the scent about. The scent produced by this gland is very attractive to other bees; it is most attractive to hive mates but is also attractive to bees from other colonies.

From these various factors, then, the bees in a colony develop a common odor, and it is by means of this odor that one bee recognizes another as either a member of the family or an intruder. Guard bees rush up to a bee alighting on the board in front of their hive and inspect the arrival with their sensitive smelling antennae. A proper smell—and the judge of what is the proper smell is the guard—allows the arrival to enter. An improper smell is likely to spell trouble for the visitor. Odors are also used as an alarm signal. Disturbed bees emit a scent from the abdomen that signals the alarm to their nest mates.

Bees do no not "hear" airborne sounds but probably "feel" sound as vibrations coming to receptors in their legs through the surface on which they stand, or as vibrations detected by the antennae. We have already noted that sound may be produced by bees' flight muscles and received as vibrations during the wagging dance. Agitated bees make sounds that may be received as vibrations by their nest mates. It has been shown that individual bees can be attracted to a cluster of bees through the single stimulus of the vibrations produced by the cluster. Also, when new queens are being reared in a hive, the old queen or the newly emerged young queen may begin to produce sounds called piping. Other young queens, either also emerged or still in their cells, answer with their own piping. The sounds produced by one queen are thought to be received by others as vibrations. The calling and answering evidently serve the purpose of notifying individual queens of the location of rivals and may lead to battles between them, or to the killing of those in the cells by the emerged queen. This area of sound production, reception, and purposes is little understood and some interesting facts about it may be waiting to be discovered. Less than fifty years ago the bees' astonishing system of communication by means of dances was completely unknown. Who knows what yet remains to be discovered?

We have noted that more than just food is passed around the colony through food transfers. Pheromones are also distributed in this way and these chemicals are extremely important in organizing the individual bees into a cohesive whole. If a honeybee queen is removed from a colony, her absence is very quickly realized by the colony members. Within a short period, sometimes within a half hour, the bees begin to act in what is called a characteristic "queenless" manner. They are restless, disorganized, and run about in a very excited manner—looking for the queen, we are tempted to think. Within a few hours after the queen's disappearance they typically begin to make emergency queen cells. They remodel worker cells in which very young larvae are present and thereafter treat these as they would queens developing in normal queen cells. If all goes well one of these will eventually emerge as a young queen and take the place of the old queen in the colony.

If, when the old queen dies or disappears, the colony contains no queen brood, young queens, young larvae to be converted, or eggs, the bees usually cannot produce a queen replacement. In this case some of the workers that may have had weak ovary development now begin egg laying. These eggs, being unfertilized, develop into drones and thus do not prolong the life of the colony. Very occasionally a queen has actually been found to develop from one of these worker-laid eggs, but this is considered a most exceptional happening. These exceptions, however, tend to occur more often in some races than in others.

With 20,000 to 80,000 bees present in one colony, how can the absence of a single bee, the queen, become apparent throughout the colony within a very few hours of her disappearance? Why do workers suddenly begin producing eggs within a short time after the loss of a queen? The answer to these two questions, it is becoming increasingly apparent through recent research, is the effect of pheromones produced by a honeybee queen.

A queen is very attractive to the bees within her colony. As she moves about on the combs, the workers in the areas through which she passes feed her and eagerly lick her body. From her body these bees derive the pheromones, and through food-sharing among the workers these chemicals soon make their way throughout the colony. The presence of these pheromones signals to the workers that all is well in the colony. Its absence has the opposite effect.

Originally it was thought that a single material, known as queen substance, produced by the queen's body had this regulatory effect. It is now realized that more than one pheromone is secreted by her body. When these pheromones are present in the colony in sufficient quantities they not only inhibit the workers from building queen cells but also inhibit the development of the workers' ovaries. Experiments have shown that a queen must be present in a colony a minimum of seven hours a day for sufficient pheromones to be produced and transmitted to prevent workers' ovaries from developing. Apparently, when a queen is old and failing, her production of pheromones may fall below the minimum level, causing the workers to build supersedure cells from which new queens will develop to replace the old queen, although the dowager is still present in the colony. The production of young queens in order that the colony may divide by swarming may come about because of the size of the colony. It may have grown so large that the amount of pheromones is not sufficient for the numbers present and thus becomes diluted below the minimum effective level, or the transmission of pheromones among the colony members is incomplete because there are too many of them.

Even if an insufficiency of pheromones causes the production of young queens in order that the colony may divide by swarming, how do we explain what triggers the act of swarming? Probably it results from crowded conditions in the hive, but who actually starts the procession? How has it developed that it is the old queen who leaves the hive? This is certainly not the case with other social insects. Perhaps it is a holdover from an absconding habit of the bees' ancestors, but this is conjecture. What decides which bees will accompany the old queen? A great deal has been learned within the last fifty years about the forces and substances that bind the thousands of individuals of a honeybee colony into a cohesive whole, but there are still more questions to be answered than questions that have been answered. One of the many answered questions was the means by which a swarm of honeybees chooses the location for its new home. The answer to this reveals a striking example of the honeybees' ability to use their instincts and their limited learning ability to work smoothly and successfully together, sometimes 30,000 or more strong.

A swarm of bees, as it leaves the hive, consists of thousands of bees with one queen. The entire group soon comes to rest on a bush, tree, or other object and alights there, one atop another, in a great mass. Scout bees begin their search for a nesting site. These scouts oftentimes have been searching for sites for several days prior to the time the swarm left the hive. As possible locations are found the scouts return and on the surface of the cluster itself they begin to dance, advertising their choice of nesting location. And, as with dances for food sources, the vigor and length of the dancing period provide the other bees with an indication of the quality of the find. Other bees follow the directions given and fly out to investigate for themselves. If they are impressed they return to dance in favor of the location. The decision is not made hurriedly, however. Sometimes many locations are advertised, up to twenty or more. Some bees will dance for one location but will change their minds after examining another advertised home. Eventually more and more of them become convinced of the desirability of one site and dance for it. With the combined brains of almost all the group working on the problem, eventually the best site is chosen. Some of the factors taken into consideration are size, lack of drafts, food resources nearby, and distance from the parent colony —enough distance to prevent sharing the same foraging area is desirable. Once the decision is fairly unanimous the swarm sets forth and moves into its new home. A great deal of discussion has gone on, everyone who so desired has had her say, and the decision has been a democratic one.

Honeybees share our world but they interpret it and react to it in a manner very different from ours. The honeybee tastes not only with her mouth but with her antennae and feet, differentiates between her friends and enemies by their smell, "loves" her mother because she tastes so good, "dances" to "talk," tells her way by the sun or by polarized light which man cannot see, discerns ultraviolet light as a color, substitutes the force of gravity for the sun's location within the darkness of the hive, and relates distance through movements. We can, here and there, catch glimpses into the honeybees' world, and any insights we thus gain can only convince us that the bees, although small in size and endowed with what we would consider limited brain power, are among the most interesting, involved, and successful of nature's creations.

Part Three

THE ANTS

CHAPTER 17

Ant Species and Development

Few other creatures have been as successful as ants and man, and it is even conceivable that the ants' success will outlast man's. Evidently the ants are here to stay—they have already been around a great deal longer than any of our ancestors. Some 35 million years ago, in the part of the world that is now Scandinavia, a coniferous type of trees grew, and down the tree trunks resin dripped from time to time. Ants and other insects sometimes became trapped in this gummy substance and there died, entombed in what today we call Baltic amber. Occasionally pieces of this fossil resin are found that contain, well preserved, the ants trapped so long ago. From these records scientists have learned that those ancient ants were structurally similar to the ants of today. There were castes of ants—that is, ants had evolved to fill certain positions in the ant societies that existed even then. Scientists consider that, in order to have reached this advanced state 35 million years ago, ants must have been evolving over a good many million years previous to that time. It was therefore generally believed that the ants as a group were at least 50 million years old.

In 1967 two recently discovered fossil ants were scientifically described. These were two very primitive worker ants found in amber collected in New Jersey. Most amazingly the material that entombed them is considered to be derived from the Upper Cretaceous age; therefore these two ants must have lived approximately 100 million years ago! Through the discovery of this highly significant fossil by two rock collectors, and its subsequent study by myrmecologists, the age of the ant group has suddenly and dramatically been doubled.

Today ants are among the most numerous of terrestrial creatures. Approximately 5000 species of them have been described and more species are being added in the scientific literature each year. The number of individuals of each of these species is incalculable. A single colony of one particular species of ant has been known to attain the fantastic population of 20 million individuals—and these were the offspring of a single mother!

Ants as a group have adapted themselves to such a wide range of living conditions that we find them on all land surfaces except permanently frozen areas. They are found from the Sahara to the Arctic Circle, from islands to jungles, and from wilderness areas to the centers of the largest cities. They are excluded only from the Arctic, the Antarctic, and the highest, coldest mountaintops. Wherever they live they take advantage of every possible type of nesting area. They are found living on the ground's surface; in the soil, some extending their homes to a depth of 20 feet or more; in and on plants, from the roots up to the very treetops; and in man-made locations such as buildings, ships, and airplanes. In these locations they prepare their nests by digging subterranean tunnels, cutting cavities in plants, building mounds, weaving leaves together, manufacturing carton (a material similar to the paper made by wasps), or, taking the easy way, by moving into a nest already built by other ants or by termites.

The ants have also adapted to take advantage of all types of food. Some ants are largely predaceous, living on a diet of meat; some are vegetarians, collecting seeds for food; others depend largely on the sugary secretions produced by plants and obtained directly from the plants or as waste products of aphids; still others grow their own fungus for food; and some are not particular, eating a variety of animal and plant foods, including man's foodstuffs.

Not only are ants as a group ancient on the earth, numerous, widespread, and highly adaptable as to living and food conditions, but they are also completely social. There are no solitary species of ants. Unlike the bees and wasps, which do have their solitary species, ants are never found living alone. The only exception to this is that when a queen in certain species founds a new colony, she forsakes her social instincts and, sealing herself in a crevice or niche, lives a solitary life until her first young develop.

The ants consist of a single family, the Formicidae, of the order Hymenoptera and are divided into eight subfamilies—or slightly more, depending on the authority you wish to follow, as scientific opinions on this matter vary somewhat. One of these subfamilies, the Sphecomyrminae, has just been designated, and its sole member is the new fossil ant discovered in amber in New Jersey. This fossil has been named *Sphecomyrma freyi.* Within this one family, the Formicidae, then, have evolved 5000 or more species, each adapted to take advantage of a particular niche in the environment. This has allowed the ants as a group to make use of a wide range of living conditions and food resources, and this highly successful evolution has concentrated not so much upon the adaptation and differentiation of the individual ants as upon their social and living habits.

Ants, like bees and wasps, are members of the large order Hymenoptera. In contrast to their distant relatives, the ants have chosen a primarily pedestrian way of life, with only the sexual forms coming equipped with wings, and these being soon lost in the case of the fertile females or queens. In a few species only one of the fertile forms may have wings. Members of the worker caste among the ants never have wings. The ants can be easily differentiated from their relatives by two distinctive characteristics. First, all ants have elbowed antennae. The first joint of the antenna (that which is attached to the head) is elongated in the females and is called the scape. The remainder of the antenna, known as the funiculus, is made up of several shorter joints. The funiculus can be folded against the scape and this articulation produces the distinctive "elbow." The second definitive characteristic is the division of the abdomen into two parts, with the first division being a narrow, one- or two-jointed pedicel with a tubercle (or tubercles) on the top; this tubercle, or swelling, distinguishes ants from the bees and wasps. The remainder of the ant's abdomen is known as the gaster. The pedicel provides the ant with a highly articulated "waist," allowing mobility of the abdomen.

Ants come in many colors and styles. Most ants are brown, yellow, reddish, or black. Others are green or blue, some are combinations of colors, and a few have a metallic sheen. Beyond the basic body design the ants are varied from species to species by differences in size, body sculpturing, hairs, spines, and pits, and are varied even within castes of the same species by development of certain body features such as enlarged jaws, strangely shaped heads, large eyes, and other such differences. Ants also come in various sizes, from the very small workers only a millimeter in length in some species, up to workers approximately an inch in length in other species.

Ants have a well-developed sense of smell and touch located in the antennae. Some ants have large compound eyes and sight is of importance to them, but other species are completely blind. Many have stings, but others have evolved beyond this point and do not have them, but have the ability to secrete acids which they use in their defense. Some species have what is known as a stridulatory organ, which is located on the pedicel and adjoining gaster, or between the two joints of the pedicel when two joints are present. This organ is composed of a row of chitinous ridges on one segment and a hard point on the second segment. The point when rubbed across the ridges causes the production of sound, which is in some cases audible to man. Other ants are thought to receive the sound through vibrations of the surface on which they are resting.

The ant's hands are her mandibles, for with her mouthparts, sometimes aided by her front legs, she carries out a multitude of duties. The mandibles kill, crush, chew, cut, carve, clean, and carry. They are the tools of the colony. Ants do not have glands that produce a wax supply for the colony as do the honeybees, nor do they make paper cells as the social wasps do.

Removal of a protecting rock resting on the soil sometimes discloses portions of an ant nest such as this ant "nursery." Workers are preparing to remove the young to chambers in the soil below. In the center front are a few larvae; the other young pictured are enclosed pupae.

Lacking such qualifications, they have no cradles for their babies. The ant young are left lying on the floor, stacked in the corner, or sometimes held in the workers' mouths for periods of time. The ants do not maintain a certain warmth in their nest through their own metabolism as do the bees, but they often build their nests to take advantage of heat, as by catching the sun's rays on a mound and thus heating its interior. When surface temperatures become too warm, they may take advantage of the cooler temperatures to be found deep underground. They therefore move their brood, carrying them with their mouthparts, from place to place in the nest to gain the optimum temperature for the young. Because the young are not permanently placed in bed in cells but can indeed benefit from being moved about, the ants' mouthparts, in addition to their many other duties, serve the valuable function of manipulating and carrying the young. It is interesting to consider that the mouthparts which can pierce the hard, chitinous armor of an enemy and kill it can also be gentle enough to carry and care for the relatively soft-skinned ant young.

Ants can swallow only liquids; therefore they chew any solid food, allow digestive juices to flow over it, and then take up the resulting liquid with their tongues. The ant has below the mouth opening a chamber known as the infrabuccal pocket. Here are collected any small pieces of semisolid food that have reached the mouth. On the jaws are combs through which cleaning organs on the legs are drawn in order to remove collected detritus from them. This material also finds its way into the infrabuccal pocket. In this pocket any liquid contained in the material present is pressed out and swallowed. The dry pellet remaining is discarded.

A very important part of the ant's anatomy is her crop, or "social stomach," in which liquids are stored. These stores may eventually pass through the valve called the proventriculus, thus continuing on into the ant's stomach where they will be digested, or the food may be regurgitated and given to other members of the colony. Since ant nests lack storage cells of any type, liquids are stored only in the crops, and thus the crop and the proventriculus, which is capable of prolonged closure without exhaustion, are organs important to the ants' social way of life.

Actually the lack of cells, which are expensive in terms of material and labor, is not a drawback but rather an advantage to ant colonies. Ants have what the human businessman would call low overhead. The energy that would be spent were the ants to build cells—and it would be considerable—can instead be diverted to other more profitable uses. Nor are the ants as tied to one location as are the bees and wasps. If conditions are unfavorable the ants can move out, carrying their young with them, and in short order set up their housekeeping elsewhere. The social wasps and honeybees have a great deal more to lose if forced out, including comb and brood that would have to be left behind.

In their development ants, like bees and wasps, undergo complete metamorphosis. The individual ant egg is very small; objects called ant eggs sold as fish food are not what they are advertised to be but are actually ant pupae, which are much larger than the eggs from which they originated. Most ants are rather constantly tending their young, and this includes licking the eggs. This licking helps prevent molds from growing on the eggs and also makes them sticky so that they are loosely held together in clumps and can be moved about the nest in these packets.

From the eggs develop larvae—wormlike, eyeless, legless grubs that resemble miniature crooknecked squash, with the mouthparts located at the narrow, bent end of the creature. This is the eating stage of the young, for it is at this time that the ant attains its growth. As a pupa it does not eat or grow but simply changes into its adult form during the pupal period; once emerged as an adult, it is its final form and size. The larvae are fed, moved about, and cared for by the adults of the colony. The food fed to the young depends to some extent upon the food habits of the adults; in some cases regurgitated liquids are the formula and in others bits of solid food are given to be chewed by the larva's mouthparts. The larvae produce secretions that are a most important attraction for the nursemaids.

The pupal stage in ants may be passed within a cocoon, or it may be a naked stage, depending on the species. The cocoon is spun by the larva, using glands near the mouth. As this stage approaches, workers bury the young in loose dirt in the nest so that the strands of silk may be attached to bits of dirt to help in the spinning process. Once the cocoon is completed, the larva is disinterred and returned to a chamber in the nest. Inside, the body of the ant is being reorganized into the adult form. The pupal stage completed, the ant either emerges from its covering on its own or, as often happens, is aided in making its escape by workers. Those undergoing a naked pupal stage are strange, completely white, quiet creatures and one can see their legs and other body parts gradually take form. Their eyes are the first portion of the body to take on any color and these are dark spots on their light bodies as they develop. A young adult

Adult Novomessor *ants move about, rearranging and caring for their young, in a cut-away observation nest at the Arizona–Sonora Desert Museum near Tucson, Arizona. The comma-shaped young are larvae; the dark-eyed, white-bodied young are pupae, which in this ant undergo a naked pupal stage.*

upon completing its pupal stage is briefly somewhat lighter in color than the older adults and in this stage is referred to as a callow.

Upon emerging from its pupal stage an ant has a definite body form that determines what function it will fulfill within the colony. There are, of course, two fertile forms, the males and the fertile females or queens. The bulk of the colony is made up of the workers, which are "stunted" females and, like their social-wasp and social-bee counterparts, never mate but devote their lives to caring for their queen-mother and for her numerous offspring—their sisters and an occasional batch of brothers.

Among the ants we find a new and further development not realized among the wasps and bees—the specialization within a species of some members of the worker caste for certain jobs, with this specialization carried to the point that the body form is modified to suit the particular job. This variation of physical form within a single caste greatly complicates attempts to understand the "hows" of the ants' physical development. Within the worker caste of some species we may find all workers with the same body form but varying in size from the very small to the very large, and with their duties varied according to their size. In other species there may occur normal, average workers, but also a second group of workers, which are much larger and are equipped with oversized jaws especially valuable for fighting or for crushing seeds; these ants are referred to as soldiers. Other types of specializations may occur. For example, among some plant-dwelling ants, soldiers with very strangely shaped heads may be present. These heads are especially adapted to be placed in the hole in the limb or plant that is the entrance to the ants' nest and so to be the protectively camouflaged cork in the bottle that prevents undesirable creatures from entering the nest.

The ants, like the social wasps and social bees, have almost but not quite done away with the need for the male of the species. They have managed to exclude the males from their societies for the greater part of the year. The winged males are produced, along with winged females, at a favorable time of year, usually early summer or midsummer. In order to take part in the nuptial flight, the males fly away from the nest, do not return, and soon die.

The female ants destined to become queens are also produced at a favorable time of year, in conjunction with the rearing of the males. In most species these future queens are a great deal larger than their worker sisters, are winged, and have an enlarged thorax to house the muscles that move the wings. Like the males, they fly away from the colony at the designated time for the nuptial flight and, except in rare cases, do not return to the home nest.

An ant colony starts with a queen. There are many variations, but the so-called normal way in which a colony is started is by the following procedure. Mature, stable colonies usually produce both fertile males and fertile females during the same period. Something triggers mass flights of these special ant forms, this something probably being weather conditions. In the desert these flights normally take place in midsummer, often just preceding, or more often following, a summer rainstorm. Many of the sexual forms of a single species from a number of different nests in a particular area usually fly at the same time; sometimes they leave their nests simultaneously on several different occasions within a period of a few days. These flights from many different nests at the same time allow cross-fertilization between colonies. When the time for the flight arrives the winged forms emerge from the nests, accompanied by large numbers of workers. The group mills about the opening to the nest and great excitement is evident. Soon a winged form can be seen flying away, and then more and more leave, until finally the excitement abates and the workers return to the nest, having had a brief spectator's part in the action.

The males and females meet during the flight and mate. They return to earth, the male's purpose fulfilled and his life nearing its end. The queen's career is just beginning. The queens may mate more than once at this time, but following this period they never mate again—the only exception being the army ant queens, which may mate again, although not too frequently. Stored within the body of the queen is sufficient sperm to last her for her lifetime of egg laying—and some queens have been known to live fifteen years! Research showed that one leaf-cutter queen had a store of sperm estimated at approximately 319 million. At least some ant queens, then, live much longer than even honeybee queens and consequently must store fantastic numbers of sperm in their bodies.

Following her flight, the queen breaks, rubs off, or otherwise discards her wings. She finds a suitable niche in which she can start her colony—under a rock, under bark, in a cavity in the earth or in a plant, or in some other location, depending on the nesting habits of her species. Within this location she remains and soon begins laying her eggs; except in the more primitive ants she does not leave this location while her first brood develops. The "usual" thing is for an ant queen to do this entirely alone, but in some species of more advanced ants several queens may band together in the same niche and establish their colonies together. The muscles that moved the queen's wings are now useless for this purpose and her body breaks them down, making the material in them available for her nourishment and for the manufacture within her body of food for the larvae. These first larvae are therefore fed on secretions from the queen's body. In addition, in some species the queen may feed the young some of her eggs, and she too may eat a portion of them. Once the ants of the first brood reach maturity they venture from the nest, forage for food, and take over all the other work of the colony except the queen's egg-laying duty.

This, as we indicated, is an "average" or "normal" way of founding an ant colony, but as a piece of music begins with a theme and then presents variations on that theme to add interest, so do the various species of ants perform many variations upon this colony-founding theme, thereby increasing its complexity and its fascination for the human ant-watcher.

CHAPTER 18

Ant Homes

As in their colony-founding habits, so also in their nest-building and food-acquisition habits the ants as a group demonstrate the old adage that variety is the spice of life. Various species of ants build homes by excavating in soil or wood, by constructing mounds, by building paper or adobe dwellings, by hollowing out the interiors of individual thorns and moving into them, and by gluing or weaving leaves together, using their young as glue bottles.

There are also some ants that do not build any kind of nest. These are the army ants, which have no permanent homes. They spend much of their time moving from one location to another and so simply choose a desirable site, as under tree roots or in a cavity, and bivouac there until ready to move on.

The majority of ants live in the soil. Using their feet and mandibles, they excavate tunnels and chambers and carry the soil to the surface, where it may be taken some distance from the nest entrance, may be dropped about the entrance, gradually forming a crater, or may be purposely built into a mound rising above the underground portion of the nest. Where a mound is built, materials in addition to soil are often added, such as pebbles or pine needles and other plant debris. Within the mound itself are built chambers and tunnels. The mound serves as an extension of the nest and is often valuable as a part of the home that is readily warmed by the sun. It is therefore often used as an incubator for the brood during the daytime. Some species build exceptionally large mounds, up to 5 or 6 feet in height.

Ants usually line the passageways and galleries of their earthen nests by agglutinating soil with a copious flow of saliva. Some tropical ants construct their nests completely in this way. Bits of soil are carried up into a tree and there glued together to build an earthen or adobe nest. After a time plants often take root in these nests and provide an efficient camouflage.

In the tropics occur ant species which build carton nests constructed from plant materials worked by the ants. From the standpoint of this carton-nest building habit these ants resemble certain termites and wasps, also able builders using converted vegetable materials.

In a similar manner some ants mix their saliva with vegetable materials to form carton, or paper similar to that made by wasps. Tropical species will construct exposed nests in trees entirely out of this material. Or, in the tropics and to some extent out of the tropics also, some ants use carton in building nests in protected locations, as in tree hollows or in the soil. These are irregular constructions, unlike the geometric paper cells sometimes covered by paper envelopes, that are made by wasps.

Many ants live in locations afforded them by plants. Some, such as the carpenter ants, excavate passageways and galleries in rotten wood. Unlike the termites, the ants do not eat the wood but simply carve in it. Rather than excavating their own living areas in plants, some ants will use cavities abandoned by other insects or will move into conveniently preformed plant cavities, such as galls, seedpods, or spaces between the overlapping leaves found on some plants. It is an ant species that lives in a twig or small branch which has the "head door" or "janitor" soldiers. A member of the colony, on approaching the "door," taps it with her antennae. The "door" backs up, the arrival enters, and the "door" closes by stepping back into place.

Among the most interesting of the plant-dwelling ants are the members of the genus *Pseudomyrma* which live in thorns of certain acacia trees in tropical America. On these trees are many large thorns, 2 inches or more in length and arranged as pairs, so that a single pair resembles the headdress of a longhorn steer; hence the common name for the plant—bullhorn acacia. The *Pseudomyrma* ants gnaw a single hole near the tip of

The adaptable ants make their homes in many diverse locations. One of the strangest of the ant homes is that made in a thorn. Certain ants hollow out the interiors of large thorns on bullhorn acacia trees and live within them. Here a thorn has been pulled open, exposing a worker, larvae, and two winged sexual forms. On many of these trees all of the thorns seem to be occupied.

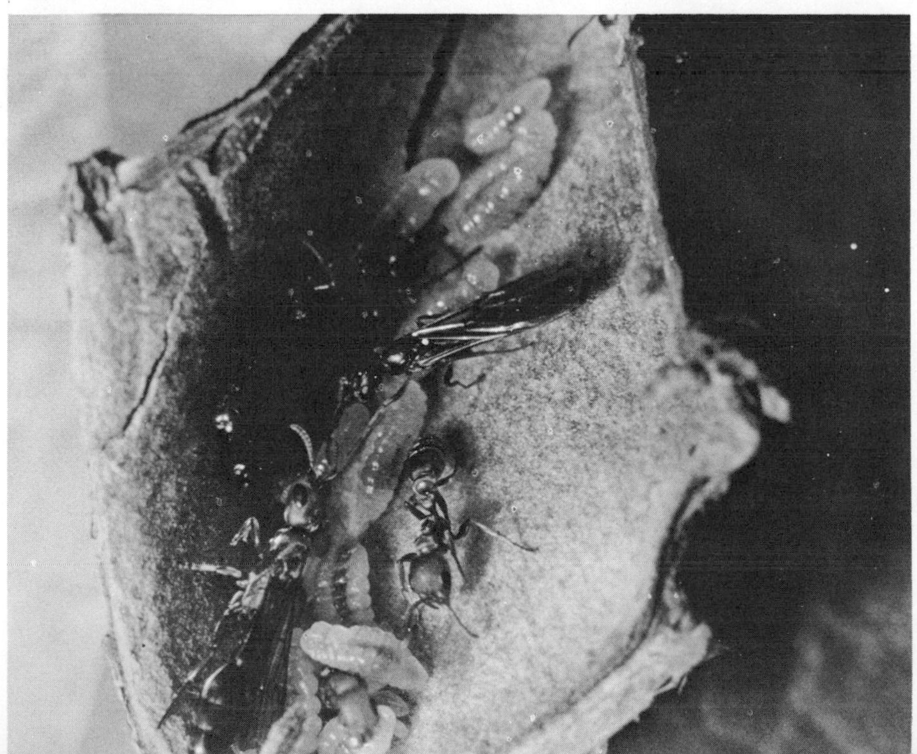

Tailor ants construct unusual nests composed of leaves held together by silken material exuded by the larvae of the colony. In ancient times the Chinese wrapped such nests in cloth, transported them to citrus orchards, and there uncovered the nests and hung them in the orchards to act as biological controls against certain damaging insects.

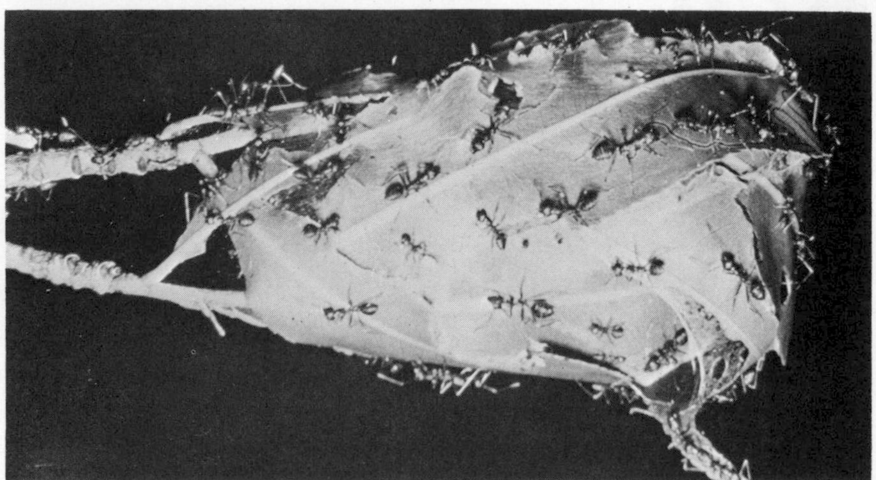

Using their mandibles and feet, tailor-ant workers pull the edges of leaves together, holding them in place. Other workers will bring larvae, carrying them in their jaws, to the site. The larvae, exuding silk, will be carried back and forth across the point where the leaves are being joined, gradually tying the leaves together and forming a part of the ant nest. A silken seam is seen in the bottom left of the photograph.

one of the pair of spines while it is yet green. They hollow out the pierced thorn and its mate, making a cozy two-room nest, always with but the single entrance. Within these thorns live small colonies of the ants, and they populate all the thorns available. The tree has glands that secrete a sweet juice eaten by these ants, and it also produces small fruitlike bodies. These have no part in the tree's reproduction—flowers are produced by the tree for this purpose—but they form another food source for the ants. These ants, which are present in large numbers on the trees, are possessed of a highly potent sting, are belligerent, and rush to the attack if their tree is jostled. They therefore provide the tree with some protection from grazing animals, leaf-cutting ants, and certainly forever after from man, once he has stumbled into such a tree. Some people believe that the tree may have evolved these special food sources in order to gain the protection given by the ants, who rely on the food. Other observers tend to be skeptical of this interpretation. Regardless of the cause, the effect is the same—the trees do have a highly efficient police force ever ready to rush to the defense of their colonies and hence secondarily to provide a degree of defense for the tree.

Perhaps the most amazing nests built by any ants are those formed of leaves held together by silk. The most famous of the ants that do this type of building is *Oecophylla smaragdina,* found in southern Asia, northern Australia, and New Guinea. Worker ants pull together the two edges of a single leaf or the edges of nearby leaves. If the span is narrow enough, an ant may grip one edge in her mandibles and pull the other edge to it with her feet. Often the distance is greater, and so a chain of ants, each ant gripping with her mouth the waist of the ant ahead of her, bridges the gap and by concerted effort pulls the two leaf edges together. Many such chains may be required. Once the leaves are being held firmly in place, other workers emerge from an established nest, each carrying a larva with the larva's head directed forward. The larva, all the while exuding a silk from glands in its head, is moved back and forth by the worker along the leaf joint. Many ant young use this silk to spin cocoons about themselves, but in this species it has been diverted to other purposes. After numerous applications of silk by many larvae, the seam is completed and a portion of the nest has thus been built. This is one of the extremely rare instances in nature in which a creature other than man is known to use a tool. We have noted that the *Ammophila* wasp is another example. Certainly these ants and other similar species did not logically determine this clever method of nest building, and it is challenging to contemplate how such a behavior pattern evolved. A further matter for amazement is that although the workers of this species are yellowish-red and the males brown, the queens are described as grass-green. One is led to hypothesize that the queen's color affords her protective camouflage as she establishes her colony in the open on the green leaves, where she is forced to expose herself until workers plus larvae are available to establish a proper home.

CHAPTER 19

Hunter Ants

The ants are exceeded only by man in the range of methods by which they obtain a living. Ants can be divided into such human professions as hunters, harvesters, dairymen, farmers, and jacks-of-all trades. Certain of them can be classified under the less savory human terms of thieves, parasites, beggars, and slave-holders.

The first ants were hunters and many of them remain so. Today it is among the most primitive types of ants that hunting is the main or sole means of livelihood. For a look at some of the hunters we turn to the Ponerinae, the ant subfamily considered to contain the most primitive of the living ants, both structurally and socially. Ants are thought to have evolved from a wasp ancestor and in many ways the ponerine ants are still close to this prototype. As the early ants evolved and spread about the earth many millions of years ago, some of them reached Australia. Later this area became isolated from other land surfaces and the ants and other animals who had arrived there earlier continued their development in this isolation. We can see today what happened to the larger animals—they did not evolve beyond the very primitive mammal stage, and there are mammals that lay eggs and then nurse their young by exuding milk through pores in the skin, and also marsupials, or pouched animals, such as the kangaroos. The primitive ants already resident in Australia changed relatively little from their forbears. Primitive ant stocks in other parts of the world evolved along numerous varied lines and many of them changed a great deal from their ancestral stock. Today Australia has the finest representation of the ponerines, and hence of primitive ants, in the world. Ponerines are present in large numbers in other parts of the world, but only in Australia are they the dominant group of ants.

Ponerines are hunters, meat eaters with no thought of a vegetable diet. They may occasionally lap up sweet plant juices, but it is meat that they consider their proper food and they obtain it by hunting, some species specializing on specific prey, as termites. Their colonies are usually small and their nests are located in the soil, or occasionally in logs. They have a powerful sting and are well known for their ability to use it.

These ants do not show the specialization among the members of the colony found in more advanced species. It is often difficult to tell a ponerine queen from the workers, as they are usually of approximately the same size. In fact, in some colonies there does not even seem to be a true queen, but rather a worker-queen. However, most species do have a queen that bears wings, takes part in a nuptial flight, and then establishes her colony.

With the exception of one known species, the ponerine queens, betraying their primitive nature, do not remain sealed in their new home but venture out from it to hunt for food for themselves, and for the young when they reach the larval phase. Feeding is about all the mother does for these young. She drops her eggs here and there, giving them little or no attention. When the larvae appear they are of more interest to the mother and later to the workers, for the young produce body exudates which the queen and workers enjoy. The young are fed in a most ungracious manner, pieces of insects being dropped near them which they devour on their own. In some species there may be some feeding of the larvae by regurgitation on the part of the adults, but generally the babies eat raw meat. In fact, so fierce are they that they may eat their sister larvae, if they can get through the long hairs or protuberances that provide some protection. The pupal stage is passed in a very tough cocoon, another protective measure, and the adult emerges without any outside assistance, though this assistance is often necessary in more highly evolved ants. Upon emerging the adult is able to care for itself completely and must do so, for its mother and older sisters would have no compunctions about devouring the new arrival if it appeared to be easy prey. In such a society the queen may continue to go out and forage for herself, and each ant acts very much according to her own dictates, with only a rather weak social order being preserved.

The most famous ponerine ants are species collectively called bull-dog ants, of the genus *Myrmecia,* almost completely confined to Australia. These are long—up to 1 inch in length, often colorful, equipped with long mandibles with which they bite, and with a very well-developed sting. They are unusual among the ponerines in that they sometimes live in large colonies of 1000 or 2000 individuals. They are well known to the Australians in the areas where they occur, as they not only defend their nest but sometimes take the offensive, chasing the human intruder 20 to 30 feet from the nest—some species, with a specialized approach, leaping several inches at a time.

The largest ant living today is a ponerine with the fitting name of *Dinoponera grandis*. It measures a little over 1 inch in length and lives in the South American rain forests. These ants make up small colonies of 100 or fewer individuals, with their nest in the soil. They live on insect food and are well equipped as hunters, with long legs, heavy jaws, and potent stings. There is probably no queen, various workers laying the eggs. A sting from this giant is quite painful and these ants are consequently not popular with the native people.

Ponerines are found in tropical areas around the world, where they are often forced to compete with other more evolved ants. In the tropics, however, there are many different food sources and environmental niches and so the ponerines have been able to survive. Some of them have remained dominant, aggressive species. Others have adopted a secretive, inoffensive manner of living that has helped them to survive. In temperate climates there are fewer nesting and food possibilities, and there the ponerines have either not survived or have survived by developing some specialty or assuming some way of life that reduces the competition with other animal species. Certain of these temperate-zone ponerines have, for example, taken up an underground, retiring, fugitive way of life. One of these species is *Stigmatomma pallipes,* which lives completely underground, on prey captured in the soil and under forest litter. The workers are probably completely blind and never reach the surface of the ground. The fertile forms emerge only when mating is to take place, the queens quickly retiring underground once again.

We cannot but admire the magnificent, seemingly defiant, and completely confident Australian bull-dog ants. They appear to be, in human terminology, a strong and proud race. And we cannot help feeling a little regret that many of their close relatives have been forced to a furtive life. There is, of course, no recognition on the part of the ants of being either proud or furtive; they have simply adapted and evolved to fit the living conditions under which they have found themselves. Proud and furtive are man's thoughts. It is easy when looking at societies of ants to anthropomorphize and to see, instead, societies of men.

Certain terms stir the human imagination and one of these is army ant. Lurid stories have been circulated about the army ants since man first met them, a large percentage of novels about the tropics work them in somewhere, and they quite regularly add excitement to movies laid in Africa or South America. It is hard to separate fact from fiction where these ants are involved, but the one person who has done more than any other to clarify the facts is Dr. T. C. Schneirla of the American Museum of Natural History, who has spent a long period studying the army ants of the American tropics. His work has proved that truth is stranger than fiction, and although it is not always so lurid, it is certainly more interesting.

"Army ant" is a general term used to cover two groups of ants, both belonging to the subfamily Dorylinae. One group consists of the driver ants of tropical Africa and Asia, the second of the legionary ants of the Western Hemisphere. The army ants are a primitive offshoot from the ants' family tree that has developed a specialized way of life that has allowed its members to be highly successful. These ants, like the ponerines,

Blind but efficient, the army ants move in columns or masses following the odor trail of those ants that are forced into the lead. Army ants never establish permanent homes and are able to support their gigantic colonies through a highly efficient predatory mode of life.

are hunters. Unlike the ponerines, however, they live together in enormous groups—colonies of one species may contain up to 20 million individuals, but most colonies are not that large. The ability to support fantastic numbers is unusual for any type of living creature that must gain its living by predation. Food, which consists of meat in any form obtainable, from insects to vertebrates, is acquired by concentrated raids made by the colony.

The army ants maintain no permanent homes, being wandering creatures that carry out regular schedules of statary, or temporarily stationary, and nomadic phases. When bivouacking, the ants find a hollow protected place, as under tree roots, form a mass of their bodies, and within the mass keep their queen and brood. Like the ponerines, the larvae of these ants are fed pieces of meat, simply placed on or near the young; they are not fed by regurgitation as in the more highly evolved ants. The young produce body exudates which the workers lick from them. The workers of the African driver ants are blind; those of the New World legionary ants have rudimentary eyes, but these are probably useless or very nearly so, possibly detecting only light and darkness. The army ants produce winged, big-eyed males which are present in the colony very briefly and which so resemble wasps that in the past they have occasionally been mistakenly classified as such. The queens are wingless and are very much larger than the workers. The worker caste is polymorphic—that is, varying in size and form. The size of the workers varies from minims (the very smallest of workers) upward through gigantic large-jawed soldiers.

It is about the New World army ants that we have the greatest amount of information, for it is these, of the genus *Eciton*, that Dr. Schneirla has studied extensively. Colonies of *Eciton burchelli* often consist of approximately 1 million individuals. Colonies of *Eciton hamatum* are nearer 250,000. The activities of these large numbers in a colony are to a great degree ruled by the body of one ant—the queen—and yet her body is to at least some extent ruled by the remainder of the ants in her colony. As the producer of all the young within the group, the queen is the first in a series of steps that determines the cycle of activities the colony will follow. As a colony of *Eciton* moves from one bivouac to another the brood is carried with them. Because of the queen's ability to produce a large number of eggs quickly—80,000 in *E. hamatum* and 200,000 in *E. burchelli* within approximately 8 to 10 days—and then to produce no more for a definite period, the brood passes through the same stages at approximately the same time.

As the current brood, which has been carried as larvae during the nomadic phase, begins to enter the quiet pupal stage, the colony enters its statary phase, bivouacking in some protected location. The queen rests in the bivouac and her abdomen begins to swell with developing eggs. After approximately a week of resting the queen enters upon her fantastic egg-laying phase. After the ants have been in bivouac approximately 19 days these eggs begin to hatch, producing larvae. At approximately the same time the pupae which developed as the colony entered the bivouac phase begin yielding callows—young adult ants. The efforts made by the 80,000 or 200,000 callows (depending on the species) to emerge from the cocoons, the exudates on their bodies, and their hyperactivity excite the workers. When the group of callows has emerged, the excitement reaches a climax that causes the entire colony to move into its nomadic phase. Within a few days, as the excitement caused by the callows begins to wear off, the larvae that hatched at the end of the statary phase have reached a large size, are eating voraciously, and are producing quantities of exudates on their bodies which are licked by the workers and serve to excite them to continue the nomadic phase. As these larvae finish their growth and enter the pupal stage, the sensory stimuli are lessened and the colony once again returns to a statary phase. Thus these particular *Eciton* ants regularly undergo a statary phase of approximately 19 days, followed by a nomadic phase of approximately 17 days (with slight differences among the species), and the forces that regulate the cycles are directly tied to the brood which originates with the queen. However, once the larvae have entered the pupal stage, much of the colony's resources, such as food and energy, that were being directed toward the active brood, can now be directed toward the queen. As a consequence she is better fed, rested, and stimulated by their attentions, and this may cause her once again to start laying eggs, thus keeping the circle of activities revolving.

During the nomadic phase the colony moves each night, stopping late at night in a temporary camp. While resting, their bodies form a mass, each ant clinging by mouth and feet to its neighbors. Within this mass are corridors and chambers through which traffic and food deliveries flow. The queen is kept well protected inside the mass and the brood is distributed throughout much of it. This collection of ants is somewhat reminiscent of the honeybees' winter swarm, for the ants, too, move closer together for warmth and farther apart for increased air circulation and hence cooling.

The legionary or army-ant soldier pictured center front is equipped with oversized hooked mandibles, making her a formidable and efficient killing machine. To the rear of the photograph is a soldier with jaws extended, and on the right are two sizes of workers which have normal-sized mandibles.

As the ants rest in this location during the day, some groups leave on raiding expeditions to provide the main population with food. With *Eciton* ants these raids assume one of two forms, depending on the species: they may move forward in a swarm or may assume columns.

In the swarm type of organization a group of workers prepares to leave the nest vicinity. Those in the front are pushed and jostled forward by the pressure of the ants massed behind them. The ants are sightless and leave behind them an odor trail; those behind simply follow the trail. The ants in front are not fearless trail-blazers—circumstances have forced them into the lead. They may attempt to hold back or deflect to the sides. With increasing pressure from the followers and a certain reticence on the part of the forward ants, the group tends to broaden out and form a swarm which may be as much as 65 feet wide. The individual ants are small, but when advancing in a swarm they provide a formidable, blood-thirsty tide of snapping mandibles. Man and larger animals can easily escape if they are capable of movement. Not so the many smaller creatures that abound in the tropics, which are caught, carved, and carried home piece by piece, or eaten on the spot by the hunters.

In those species that hunt with a column formation the ants advance by means of a main column with smaller columns branching off. The various columns move forward, circling, meeting, and rebranching. They thus eddy about, encircling and trapping the creatures in the territory explored.

The raiders return bearing food for the stay-at-homes. That night the entire colony will once again move forward, travel throughout much of the night, and bivouac in a new location before morning. When the entire colony is moving forward the ants form a long procession, each ant detecting the path to follow by the odor left by those who have passed just ahead of her. Near the end of the procession march the workers carrying the brood, the babies held by the workers' mouths and slung under their bodies. Finally the queen marches along, her large body almost completely covered by the excited workers who clamber about her. In such a procession, or in raiding, the smaller workers tend to be concentrated near the center of the forward moving lines, with the big-headed, larger soldiers scattered along the outer edges. This placement of the fierce soldiers on the peripheries would appear to be a deliberate defensive move and was long interpreted as such. However, while it is a valuable defensive measure, it results simply from the size of the soldiers, who are tripped easily if they attempt to walk among the small workers and so are forced to the outer edges of the procession by mere mechanics.

During the statary phase, raiding groups leave the bivouac each day to return with food, but less is needed at this time than during the nomadic phase. In the statary phase, the brood usually consists of noneating pupae and eggs. During the nomadic phase, however, the already populous colony has been increased by many thousands of new adults and an equal number of hungry larvae. At this time the daily raids gain in number, size, and momentum to meet successfully the challenge of providing for the increased population.

Occasionally the brood of a legionary ant colony will be composed entirely of sexual forms. This includes a few thousand males and a very few females—less than ten. These queens have no wings. They mate with males, probably from other colonies, who seek them out, the males having large eyes and wings. Apparently the colony will favor one of the young females and will eventually split into two parts—one part accompanying the old queen, the second the one chosen young queen. The mating of the new queen takes place after this division. The remaining queens are abandoned. Thus we have a colony division arrangement that in some ways resembles that of the honeybees and is unusual among the ants. The army ant queens are unusual also in the fact that throughout their lives they mate at intervals with different males, whereas ant queens normally mate only on their single nuptial flight. The old queen of a colony may be superseded; this too is reminiscent of the honeybee.

The New World army ants contain species that move about on the surface of the ground, even some that raid in trees and form arboreal bivouacs; others spend their time under the surface of the soil, under plant litter, and actually speedily construct earthen archways under which the ants move forward. The driver ants of the Old World are primarily found living and moving under soil or plant cover or within their own covered runways. Occasionally on dull days they emerge and move forward on the surface.

Less is known about the driver ants than about the American legionary ants, as the former have not been so thoroughly studied. Some of the African driver ants, rather than having what might be termed a nomadic phase, simply emigrate to a new area at irregular intervals. For some species these migrations may last several days. The driver ants tend to be more subterranean in habit than are the legionary ants. It is thought that with the driver ants the queen may remain fat and awkward rather than regaining her figure to allow easier traveling, as is the case with the *Eciton* species. Some species of driver ants form the very largest colonies known among the ants, and the size of the broods to be fed are correspondingly large. The driver *Anomma wilverthi* has colonies with a worker population varying from 10 to 20 million individuals and a single brood may be made up of 1 million young!

The army ant's life is spent in a dark, sightless world; endless searching is its design, killing its occupation, odors and tastes its organizers, and thousands, or millions, of females its cohorts.

CHAPTER 20

Harvesters and Fungus-Growers

In low Arizona foothills lie the adobe ruins of a once active fort, which a hundred years ago offered shelter from the dreaded Apaches to early travelers as they crossed the desert. Some of the travelers arrived there only after they were dead. Their bodies were added to the populous cemetery and wooden crosses erected over them. Those who carved the crosses recorded history on them without any superfluity of words, and so we know today that long ago one unfortunate was "tied to cactus and roasted to death," while another was "staked out on ant-heap and left."

Torture by ants was not uncommon in many parts of the world, and the species of ant chosen for this type of slow death in southern Arizona is thought to have been one that is plentiful in this part of the world and is known by the generic name of *Pogonomyrmex*. Having once sat on a single, understandably irate *Pogonomyrmex,* we can conceive that death on this kind of an ant hill would be a hard way to go. The pain from one sting is quite severe and does not soon dissipate but travels, seemingly through the lymph, causing sore glands in the general area and leaving a hard, numb spot at the site of the sting for several days. Since a colony may contain several thousand individual ants, all of whom would no doubt be upset by a human staked down on their nest, the consequences would be fearful to imagine.

This *Pogonomyrmex* is but one of many ants included in the group known as harvesters. These ants have learned to use plant products for the major portion of their food supply and so have made an important advance over their more primitive cousins, the ponerines and dorylines.

For an ant, predation is a precarious means of obtaining a living. Except in the case of the specialized army ants, the ants that must hunt for and kill their food are usually limited to living in small groups, as their food supply—other living creatures—may not be present in great numbers and certainly cannot be stored for later use. By finding a more dependable food supply, plant products, certain ants have been able to live in large groups and to survive in areas that do not provide a year-round food supply, since some plant products can be stored for use during lean periods. Therefore the harvester ants collect seeds when these are available and store quantities of them in special galleries in their nests, and these seeds represent a food stock, like the bee's honey.

All the harvester ants belong to the subfamily Myrmicinae, which also contains ants following other pursuits to obtain a living. The harvesting habit was a solution to the living conditions that had been imposed upon these ants, and this solution was arrived at independently by several different groups within this one subfamily.

Some of the harvesters, as *Pogonomyrmex,* have retained their wasplike sting. Others have lost it. While grains make up the major portion of their diet, they have not entirely lost their ancestors' taste for meat, for they will use insects and other such meat sources when these are easily available. All harvesters live in nests in the ground. In colony establishment they show advances over the ponerines and army ants. Colonies are usually started by a single queen who is winged, takes part in a nuptial flight, seals herself in a location in the soil, and there remains without venturing out and thus exposing herself to danger. With her body's stored nutrients she is able to rear her first brood, which then takes over her care and that of other young. Another advance is that the larvae may be fed with pieces of seeds but are more normally fed by regurgitation, as is the queen. The workers also pass food and secretions among one another. Another major advance that has taken place in this group is that in many of the species the pupae undergo their transformation in a naked stage. They are well cared for and need no protection, such as a cocoon, as is required in the lower ants.

Since the harvesters live in arid and semiarid regions where vegetation is not lush, the craters or mounds that take shape about the entrances to their nests are rather easily seen. Some species even clear all vegetation from around their nests, making large bare areas, up to 20 feet in diameter. In the center of the bare area is located a crater, and this is often surrounded by an extensive ring of chaff or plant materials that have been removed from the nest and discarded. Occasionally a viable seed is discarded in this area around the nest and sometimes a ring of plants can be seen growing there. At one time it was thought that the ants were not only reapers but also sowers, planting crops in order to harvest the seeds. Not so; the plants grow by accident but just the same their seeds will be harvested as readily as any others in the vicinity.

Seeds are collected from the ground or the plants by the thousands of worker ants in the colony. The seeds upon being delivered to the nest are taken inside and husked. This outer covering is then taken back out of the nest and discarded on the chaff ring. The husked seed is stored in one of the "granaries" in the nest. Occasionally some of these seeds may get wet and sprout underground, in which case they are taken out and discarded. If a portion of the stores get damp they may be taken above ground, allowed to dry out, and then returned to the underground chambers.

When food is needed ants "chew" on the seeds, adding copious amounts of saliva. The resulting pasty mass is called ant bread and may be stored briefly. Continued chewing and addition of saliva changes the bread to soup, which may be eaten by the chewer, fed to another adult or a larva, or stored temporarily in the chewer's crop.

Some species of harvesters have a monomorphic worker caste—the workers not being differentiated by size or structure. Other species have a special soldier form with an extremely enlarged head. The enlargement is not for housing brains, but rather brawn. This impressive supply of muscles is for moving the soldier's large jaws. These jaws probably serve a dual purpose—cracking open hard seeds and defending the colony—although the relative value of and emphasis on the two activities probably vary from one species to another.

Whereas the army ants have been portrayed as rapacious villains in much of man's oral and written allusions to ants, the harvesters, as diligent reapers and storers, have been held up to man as a model to emulate. King Solomon did so in the Bible and Aesop in the fables. What better backing could an ant species get?

Those renowned gentlemen might equally well have advised errant humans—"thou sluggard!"—to look to the fungus-growing ants as examples of hard working, self-sufficient creatures. However, as the fungus-growing ants occur only in the Western Hemisphere, they were not known to the ancient writers.

These are the farmers among ants, for they actually raise their own food, and this agriculture is carried out underground in complete darkness. It consists of a single crop, fungus, grown on a substratum that the ants provide, and from this crop they obtain their entire supply of food, often maintaining colonies consisting of hundreds of thousands of individuals; estimates for some species run as high as 1 million individuals in a colony. Most of the fungus-growing ants, including the most spectacular, which belong to the genus *Atta,* live in the tropics, but a few of the smaller species have spread into more temperate areas.

A developed nest of one species of *Atta* consists of as many as a thousand underground chambers, some of the larger individual chambers being described as a yard long, a foot wide, and a foot deep. In these is raised the fungus crop. The series of chambers and passageways may extend to a depth of 15 or 20 feet, and evidence on the surface of the ground indicates that the nest may cover an area of half an acre. The earth mined from below is brought to the surface through many different openings and is dropped, forming craters. Eventually these craters may merge, forming a mass of bare soil on the surface of the ground. There may be a thousand

Fungus-growing ants carry pieces of leaves, flowers, or other similar materials to their underground nests. There the chewed plant materials are used as a base upon which the ants grow a crop of fungus; this fungus serves as their food supply. The plant material, when being transported, is grasped in the mandibles and carried elevated above the head like an umbrella. A common name for these ants is parasol ants.

or more entrances to a single nest, not all in use at once, but used from time to time as needed.

Medium-sized workers travel out from these nests through the tropical foliage along well-worn ant paths, which are cleared and are quite obvious to the human eye. Using their mandibles the workers cut whole leaves or pieces of leaves and flowers from living plants and carry these back to their nests. This practice accounts for their common names of leaf-cutter ants, or parasol ants, the latter referring to the fact that the lofty green burdens they carry in their mandibles stick up over their heads somewhat like parasols. Along one of these ant roads can be seen a steady outward stream of unburdened ants moving in one direction along the ground. The incoming traffic consists of a flow of returning ants laden with their pieces of plant material. A good-sized colony can strip a tree of its foliage in a night, on succeeding nights move on to other sources, and then return to start the cycle anew when sufficient time has elapsed to allow a new growth of leaves. For this reason leaf-cutters are highly unpopular with human agriculturists in the American tropics.

The leaves once delivered within the nest are chewed; saliva is added, oftentimes fecal material also; and the resulting material is tamped in place in the already established fungus garden. Here the material acts as a rich substratum on which the fungus grows. In starting a new garden or in adding to an old one the workers take bits of the fungus and "plant" it on the new substratum. Portions of the fungus thus grown then serve as the ants' food.

Since fungus lacks chlorophyll, that amazing green substance that allows a plant to form carbohydrates from chemical compounds in the presence of sunlight, it must obtain its nourishment from other material, in this case manured leaves. Lacking the possibility of manufacturing its own food, the fungus has no need for sunlight and can live in the darkness of the ants' underground nests. Each species of fungus-grower cultivates its own particular strain of fungus, and none of these fungi has ever been found growing outside the ants' nests. The fungi have been identified as belonging to the group known as Basidiomycetes, which also contains true mushrooms. However, the fungi grown by the ants do not form a mushroom, which is the fruiting body. Instead, under the constant care of the ants they produce slender threadlike growths called mycelia, at the ends of which are small bulbs known as bromatia. It is the bromatia that the ants eat. When grown experimentally in the laboratory, the fungi do not produce bromatia and they are often overwhelmed by other fungi

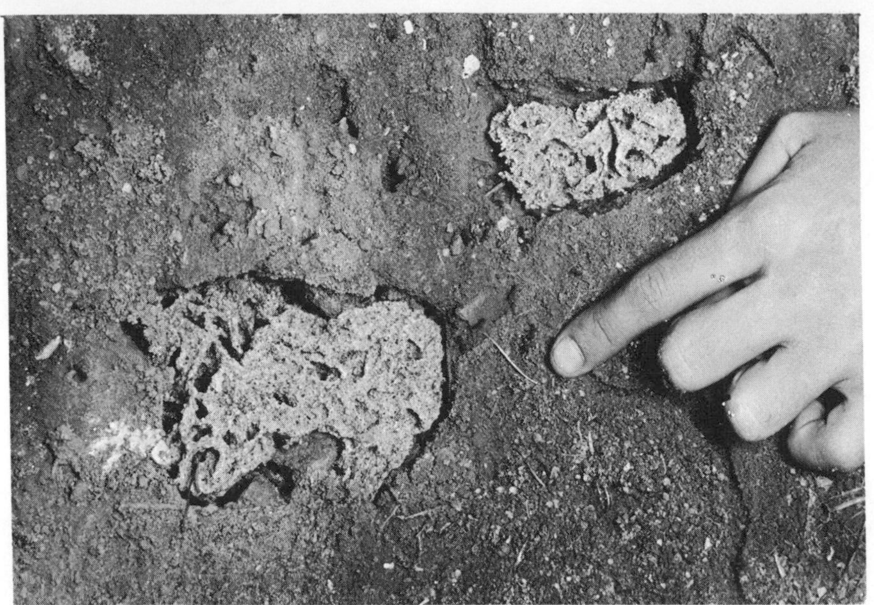

In chambers deep within the soil, ants known as leaf-cutters or fungus-growers raise fungus gardens such as the two pictured here. In some species the base for the fungus growth may be insect feces, but for most fungus-grower species the fungus thrives on a base of plant materials which are chewed by the ants, manured with their fecal matter, and influenced by their saliva. The fungus provides the sole food of the ants, and a single ant colony may support many fungus gardens.

and bacteria. The care that the ants bestow upon their fungi is plainly the factor that causes successful growth. This care consists of providing the correct substratum, rather constant inspection of the growth, provision of proper temperature and humidity by regulating entrances to the nest and by collecting material outside the nest only under optimum conditions of temperature and humidity, and, of prime importance, the addition of saliva and ant feces to the garden.

All these factors are interrelated and important. The fungus-growing ants have thus evolved to a point where their sole food source is fungi, and the evolution of these particular fungi has reached a level where they can no longer exist without the care given them by the ants. This living together of two dissimilar organisms for their mutual benefit is called symbiosis.

Among the *Atta* the workers range in size from very small (1 millimeter in length) to very large (up to 14 millimeters). A division of labor takes place as a result of the differences in size. The smallest workers stay inside the nest, tending the brood and the gardens, the medium-sized workers harvest the leaves, and the very largest are soldiers, which tend to remain inside the nest and rush to its defense when needed. Although stingless, they have powerful jaws and can inflict a painful bite.

With these ants the pantry is also the nursery, for the brood is kept in the growing crop of fungus and individual young may sometimes be well embedded in it, with the crop actually growing on them. The workers place pieces of fungus on the larvae's mouthparts and the young chew these for their food supply.

A new *Atta* colony is established by a queen, who takes part in a nuptial flight, seals herself in the soil, and begins to lay eggs. This queen brings with her a "starter" of fungus for her colony. Pieces of the fungus in the infrabuccal pocket were formerly thought to supply this starter, but it now appears that in at least some species larger pieces of the fungus garden are carried by the queens in their mouths, and these serve as the beginning of the new garden. Once inside her niche, however, the queen has no leaves on which to start her garden, nor does she have workers to bring them in. Therefore she carefully tends her tiny "starter" garden, manuring it with her own fecal material and adding broken-up eggs to provide it with additional nourishment. The queen produces two kinds of eggs. From the smaller ones workers develop. The larger eggs contain more yolk and these are eaten by the queen and by the members of the first brood. Once the first workers have matured they begin bringing in material on which to grow the fungus, and the colony begins to increase in size. The first brood is unusual in that its members develop on eggs and later, as adults, switch to a fungus diet when a supply of this material is at last available. For all later broods fungus will be both baby food and adult food. The *Atta* queens are amazing creatures, having sufficient bodily resources without recourse to outside help not only to provide food for the young but also to fertilize the developing fungus garden. Because of the evident age and the size of some *Atta* colonies it is thought that additional queens may occasionally be adopted into a colony. The fact that an *Atta* queen was found to have approximately 319 million sperm in her body indicates that a single queen may well be extremely prolific; it also indicates that she probably mates with more than a single male during her nuptial flight.

The *Atta* represent the highest development of the fungus-growing habit, but several other less highly developed species also subsist on a fungus diet. The most primitive of the fungus-growing ants use as their substratum insect feces only; others, slightly more advanced, use insect feces plus green leaves. The less advanced also have much smaller colonies and smaller nests, some of one chamber only. In two genera of the simpler fungus-growers the queens appear sometimes to leave their colony-founding cells and forage for material on which to grow their fungus. The simplest of the fungus-growers have only one size of worker; they forage singly rather than in files and become immobile when threatened, instead of taking defensive measures as do the *Atta.*

We can only conjecture how such an amazing agricultural society as the *Atta*'s developed. Perhaps long ago fungi grew on the ants' fecal matter in the nest and the ants gradually came to depend on such food. But, we wonder, how did the ants come to add other materials, such as leaves, for additional nutrients for the garden? Perhaps the fungus-growing ants were first harvesters, and fungi developing on wet seeds within the nest were then used for food. Even if we explain fungus-raising as an outgrowth of harvesting (which is strictly an unproven hypothesis), we still have to explain how the harvesting of seeds developed, and this is no easy task. It is a long jump from hunting to harvesting, and another equally long jump to planting. Some groups of men have never made the second of these two leaps.

CHAPTER 21

Herders and Honeypots

Food is where you find it and the opportunistic ants have found it in many different places. Some ants even feed on the excrement of small creatures called homopterans. These ants are called dairying ants, for to some extent they herd, protect, and care for their miniature "cattle," in addition to "milking" them. From them the ants obtain a liquid that is neither white nor milk but to the ants is equally nourishing.

Many plants produce a sweet liquid, such as the nectar in flowers, or juices from nectaries on other parts of the plant. The bees, of course, are the great gatherers of this type of food. Other small creatures, of which the best-known are the aphids, but which also include coccids, jumping plant lice, leaf hoppers, mealy bugs, and scale insects, obtain the sap from plants by drilling with specialized mouthparts directly into the plant and sucking up the liquid found therein. As the liquid moves through its body, the aphid derives substances from the plant juice for its growth, but many nutrients, especially sugars, remain in the liquid as the aphid voids it. The ants find this liquid as acceptable as any other sweet juice and readily collect it as food.

Ants may collect this so-called honeydew from the plants on which it has been excreted or may take it directly from the aphids. In the latter case the ant approaches an aphid and taps it on its back with her antennae. If all goes according to custom, the aphid will expel a drop of liquid excrement which the ant will imbibe.

Most people who have attempted to garden are familiar with aphids and their relatives. The aphids are tiny but can do a great deal of damage to plants, slowing their growth, spreading plant diseases, and causing the growth of fungi on the plant. One aphid soon leads to more, for the aphid female can produce numerous young parthenogenetically—that is, without mating. These wingless young are born alive, ready to start eating at once. The "babies" are pregnant even before birth and so the generations are produced in quick succession, up to thirty in a summer. In the fall, winged males and winged females are also produced, mating takes place, the female lays eggs, and these survive the winter. Since the aphids are unwelcome creatures as far as man is concerned, and since some species of ants further promote the already fantastic multiplication of aphids, the ants receive a certain amount of condemnation.

By the mere collection of honeydew from aphids, the ants may cause increased damage to plants, since attended aphids are believed to suck up more juice than those not being solicited for food. Some ants simply collect honeydew from aphids when they happen to locate them. Others will build earthen or carton enclosures about collections of aphids, and species of *Oecophylla* are known to make silken shelters about coccids. The ants appear to be building barns and fences for their "cows," but actually the constructions are largely for the benefit of the attending ants, although they do incidentally protect the "cows." The ants also afford some protection to the aphids or other homopterans being used by defending them from enemies, as they might defend any food source in which they were interested. Attending ants also benefit the aphids directly by removing the honeydew that might collect about them, causing them to stick in place or fungi to grow on them.

Various of the aphids, for their part, show some modifications of behavior and structure that aid the ants in obtaining the honeydew. For example, some aphids, when unattended, jet their honeydew a considerable distance away but when tended by ants extrude it slowly. Some species of aphids regularly attended by ants have a circle of stiff hairs which catch and hold the drop of honeydew as it is excreted.

There are species of ants that go even further in their care of aphids. These may keep the adults and/or the eggs within their nests, caring for them as they would their own brood. The aphids' eggs may be kept in the ants' nest all winter. A few species of ants appear to derive most, or perhaps all, of their food from aphids and coccids fed underground on roots. One particularly infamous ant is a species of *Lasius*. These ants tend the eggs of a particular aphid in their underground nest throughout

Many species of ants obtain their food by utilizing the excretions of homopterans. The latter utilize plant juices for their food, and a great deal of this liquid is excreted little-changed, much to the ants' benefit. The ants pictured are caring for white, cottony-appearing coccids in their nest located under a rock.

the winter and when the eggs hatch in the spring the ants carry the young aphids out of the nest through ant-excavated tunnels and place them on roots. There the ants tend them and collect food from them throughout the summer. Since the roots are those of corn, these highly successful dairying ants and their aphids draw down the wrath of the farmers.

The larvae of pseudococcids tended on shrubs and trees by certain ants in Java, if disturbed, may be picked up by the attending ants with their mouthparts, or may climb upon the ants' bodies and thus ride away! In one of the strangest of these weird relationships, the virgin queen of a tropical ant species, when she sets forth on her nuptial flight, carries within her mouth a young fertilized coccid. Just as the leaf-cutter queen takes her fungus "starter," this queen takes her coccid "starter"!

If we take the liberty of calling certain ants farmers, dairymaids, harvesters, and hunters, then one small group can only be called pots. These are honeypots, or repletes, who serve their nest mates simply as receptacles for the colony's extra food supplies. As such they represent one of the strangest of the adaptations that the ants have developed.

Honeypot ants represent an adaptation of some ant species to dry and inhospitable environments. Certain ants in these species become living jars or "honeypots" holding the liquid food stock of the colony. These bloated members of the colony hang suspended from the roof of the underground chambers. When the food stored in the abdomen of the honeypot is needed, the honeypot regurgitates a portion of her supply to the normal-sized members of the colony.

The honeydew-collecting ants fill their crops with the liquid that they obtain directly from plants or indirectly through aphids and other similar creatures. An individual ant will sometimes fill her crop to the extent that her gaster or abdomen is somewhat distended. Certain species carry this practice further. The workers forage for sweet liquids from plants or homopterans, return to the colony, and regurgitate their load to an ant or ants within the colony. Some of these receive so many offerings that their crops become enormously distended. While they are still able to move, they crawl to the roof of their underground chamber, and there they remain hanging from the ceiling. They are further fed by foraging workers until their gasters are completely distended, with the abdominal sclerites that formerly overlapped to protect the delicate inner covering of the abdomen resting far apart atop the round golden ball of honey. These honeypots are not a specially adapted body form of their species. Some studies show those chosen may be the largest of the workers and may be young ones, who somewhat by chance have been gradually filled with honey until they have reached this immobile state. Once hanging from the roof they will remain there, as living jars, probably for the rest of their lives. They may hold as much as eight times their own weight in honey, and if by accident they fall the inch or two from the roof to the floor, they may pop like dropped watermelons and die, while their nest mates lap up the spilled contents of the broken jar. The honey is these ants' reserve food supply, just as the seeds are the harvesters' reserve. When food is needed the honeypots regurgitate a part of their supply to be used by their thinner sisters.

The distended abdomen of the honeypot ant is translucent and golden with the stored honey. Honeypot ants are found in portions of North America, Australia, and Africa. They have often been used as a food delicacy by native peoples, the honey stored in their abdomens being quite sweet and usually delicious.

The habit of storing honey in this manner has arisen independently in three different subfamilies of ants, and species of honeypots are found in deserts or dry areas in Mexico, the American Southwest, Australia, and Africa. The habit is an adaptation to dry conditions, the liquid being stored when available and used when needed. Research has recently shown that food is passed from the foragers to the honeypots when temperatures are moderate. When the temperature reaches approximately 87° F. and the body processes of the ants are speeded up, the honeypots begin to pass the liquid back to the others of the colony. Evidently the reserves are banked in cool, moist weather and withdrawn when dry, hot weather occurs.

Honeypots have been a popular delicacy with the natives in the lands where they occur. Australian aborigines were known to relish them, as did the Mexican Indians. Either the entire ant was consumed, or the big yellow abdomen snipped off and eaten. Digging in Arizona mesa country, we found a prosperous colony of ants complete with about fifty honeypots hanging from a red, rocky, underground ceiling. The abdomen of each of these fat ladies was about 3/8 inch in diameter—golden and translucent. The honey had the aroma of orange blossoms, but the closest thing to orange blossoms in the vicinity was sagebrush. The honey was delicious.

CHAPTER 22

Parasitic Ants

The similarities between aspects of human and ant life are sometimes too close for human comfort. We tend to look with a critical eye at the next group of ants, the members of which in our terms have learned to cheat. In ant terms they have simply found successful patterns of life—ants have no moral laws.

Thief ants usually prey on other ants, stealing food supplies or brood, but the most extreme case is a tropical genus *Carebara,* which preys not upon ants but upon termites. A *Carebara* colony lives within a termite nest in which the ant workers make tunnels sufficiently large for these particular ants to travel through but too small for the termites to enter. These ant workers are less than 1/12 inch in length and, living in constant darkness, are sightless. Slipping through their special tunnels, they prey for the most part upon the young termites, killing, eating, and retreating back into the safety of the tunnels.

The *Carebara* queen, unlike her minute daughters, is sighted and winged, since she must leave the nest, be fertilized, and establish a new colony. With the copious food resources provided by their hosts, the tiny *Carebara* workers can develop a queen that, compared to the workers, is gigantic. She is heavy-bodied, may be 1 inch long, and has been estimated to be 5000 to 7000 times larger by volume than the workers. Greater differences between two members of the same sex in a species would be difficult to imagine. The queen's size is no doubt of value in her setting forth from the safety of the home nest but presents a problem. How can a giant mother tend midget babies? She doesn't. Instead, as a virgin queen prepares for flight, several of the small workers within the nest attach themselves to her legs, are carried along, and so come to dwell with her in the new nest. We have noted "starter" fungus and coccids, and now we have the ultimate—"starter" ants!

There are species of ants that have come to be permanent dwellers in the nests of other species of ants, as the *Carebara* are permanent dwellers in termite nests. These ants may carry the adaptation one step further. Instead of leading a precarious life of snatch, steal, and run, they have developed "friendly" relations with their hosts, thus obtaining not only food but a greater degree of safety than *Carebara* enjoys. An example is an ant smaller than its host, which enters the hosts' chambers through adjoining small passageways. These guests are welcomed because they clean the hosts, crawling upon them and licking them. The large ants evidently find this enjoyable, for in return they regurgitate drops of food upon request to their massagers, and so these permanent guests obtain their food supply.

Some species of ants take advantage of other species in order to establish new colonies. Whereas many queen ants are able to establish their colonies using only their own resources, in some species they rely upon aid, as do the *Carebara* queens, who carry the help with them. Some species of ants have queens that mate and may either remain in the parent nest or be adopted into another nest of the same species, more than one queen being acceptable in these colonies. From the point of accepting help from members of your own colony or species, it is only a short step to accepting or requiring help from colonies of another species, and this has happened with some species. In this case a queen, after having mated, enters the nest of a closely related species. This entrance is not an easy matter, for one species of ant is rarely friendly toward another. The trespassing queen may sneak in and hide in the nest until she acquires some of the nest odor. She may have a neutral, nonoffensive odor, unlike other members of her species, or a body odor more like her hosts' than her own relatives'. She may resemble the host. She may assume a dominant, blustering attitude, or a fawning one, feeding the hosts. She may have special glands which produce substances desired by the host colony, thus making her attractive to them. Whatever her method, if she is successful in her entry she begins to lay eggs, and these are cared for by the workers of the host colony. The original queen is eventually killed, either by the invading queen, by her young when they make their appearance, or by the demented host workers. Without the original queen the host workers are not replaced upon their death, and eventually a pure colony of the invading species results, its shady beginnings no longer evident. This we call temporary social parasitism. Some extremely complicated situations can develop. It has recently been determined that the ant *Lasius speculiventris* is a temporary social parasite on *Lasius minutus,* which is parasitic on another *Lasius* species.

Expanding upon temporary social parasitism, some ants have found it of value to keep their "help" permanently, rather than having it only during colony founding, and so enter the "masters" and the "slaves." The best-known of the slave-making ants is the European species *Formica sanguinea,* which enslaves *Formica fusca.* This latter ant is one of those that we might call a jack-of-all-trades. It hunts insects but also accepts offerings of honeydew from aphids. Being a member of the advanced subfamily Formicinae, it has lost its sting and instead has a special means of squirting formic acid at its enemies. These ants do not have any outstanding body forms specialized for particular jobs, other than having reproductives and workers. They live in colonies composed of a few hundred to a few thousand individuals, regurgitate food to the well-cared-for larvae, are tolerant enough to support several queens in a colony, and produce young queens capable of independent colony founding.

Their near relatives, *F. sanguinea,* being members of the same genus, are similar in structure, including the lack of sting. These ants too maintain several queens in a nest but also may live in communes—that is, collections of nests in one area. Such a commune consists of large numbers of ants, including many queens, and the ants in the individual nests display tolerance toward neighboring nests. It is an ant "village." The *sanguinea* queens, however, cannot independently establish their colonies. They must either remain in the home nest, move into another nest of the same species, or move in with another species. This chosen species is often *fusca,* which among its attributes or among its shortcomings, depending upon the way you desire to interpret it, has a rather nonaggressive, pacific nature and so is an easy target for exploitation.

The *sanguinea* queen, if successful in her move into a *fusca* colony, steals some *fusca* pupae, which she guards. The callows that emerge assume the *sanguinea* to be their queen and care for her eggs and young. Eventually the *fusca* queen is killed. Thus far we have temporary parasitism. But when the young *sanguinea* mature and the colony is on a strong footing, these *sanguinea* workers raid nests in the vicinity and carry home *fusca* pupae. This booty, of course, develops into *fusca* workers, thus maintaining the population of the host workers in the absence of the original host queen. These slaves, not having experienced any other situation, seem to consider their lot normal and carry on regular worker activities within the nest of their "masters." The *fusca* adults are black, which is a familiar pattern in slavery and is one of the reasons they have been termed slaves. However, whether slave in a *sanguinea* nest or a worker in a normal *fusca* colony, the life of these *fusca* workers would follow very much the same pattern.

Closely related sanguinary ants found in Asia and North America follow a life pattern similar to that of the European *F. sanguinea.* Among these slave-making ants, the number of slaves present per master has been found to vary tremendously, and in some colonies no slaves at all are maintained beyond the colony-founding period. Apparently the sanguinary ants require help to found new colonies and tend to maintain "foreign" help throughout the life of the colony, but they are not completely dependent upon it. Complete dependence is the next level.

The Amazon ants cannot live without slaves, and their bodies, brains, and social living habits are specialized for war, success in which brings them the slaves they must have. The Amazon ants include several species belonging to the genus *Polyergus,* which, like the sanguinary ants, are members of the most advanced of the ant subfamilies, the Formicinae. The Amazons, too, prey upon ants of the genus *Formica.*

The Amazon queen establishes her colony by invading a *Formica* colony and killing the rightful queen. The *Formica* workers rear the Amazon workers and when sufficient of these are present, the Amazons begin their raids against neighboring *Formica* colonies, from which they return with brood to be reared as slaves by slaves. The Amazons have mouthparts especially adapted for their raiding existence. These are long, sickle-shaped, and excellent for puncturing adversaries. When raiding, their manner is commanding, bold, aggressive, and completely warriorlike. In their nests, however, they appear helpless, leaving all the care of the nest, of the brood —both Amazon and captive—and of themselves to their efficient slaves. The Amazons do not even feed themselves but depend entirely on their slaves to procure food and regurgitate it to them. Supposedly (in terms of human logic) the Amazons are unable to care for their own brood or excavate their nests because of the outlandish shape of their mandibles. When raiding, however, they open tunnels and excavate in the enemies' nest to carry on their war, and they pick up captive brood which they carry home using their mouthparts.

Evidently over millions of years the Amazons have become adapted for a warlike existence at which they are now highly successful. Theoretically there has been no need for them to retain—and so they have lost—the instincts that would direct their independent care of themselves, their brood, and their nest—abilities that no doubt were possessed by their ancestors. These things we do not know but can only surmise.

The Amazons are obligatory slave-makers, dependent upon help to establish and maintain their colonies. They do, however, have a queen, plus a worker caste which carries out one main duty, the waging of warfare. There are other ants so completely parasitic that they do not even produce a worker caste. An African ant named *Wheeleriella santschii* produces queens that invade the nests of *Monomorium salomonis*. The *W. santschii* queen produces eggs and the young are reared by the host workers. These host workers also kill their own queen. The eggs of the new queen produce only sexual forms—no workers are produced! These sexual forms eventually leave the nest to mate, and the new queens will go on to establish new parasitic colonies. Their queen-mother is left behind in a dying colony; no workers of her own species were produced and no host replacements are available, their queen being dead.

CHAPTER 23

Organization of Ant Colonies

Poetically the Bible describes the ants as "little upon the earth" and without "guide, overseer, or ruler." Since man first began observing ants he has wondered how these creatures, most of them less than an inch in length, with a brain of proportionate size, and without a guide or a ruler could successfully live in large societies over much of the earth. Science is beginning to unravel the highly complex answers to this question, and the answers are connected with senses, instincts, learning, and various unusual means of communication.

It is with her senses that an ant receives stimuli from the world about her. To these stimuli she may react either through the use of innate responses or as a result of learning. Let us first look at the ants' senses. Some ants have well-developed eyes—although they are of a type different from man's—and to these sight is a valuable sense. Many ants, however, are sightless; they do not have eyes or their eyes are of little or no value. Such are the highly efficient army ants, and ants that spend their lives underground. The sense of smell is well developed in all ants, and it and the senses of taste and touch are probably the ones of most value to them. The ants' antennae—mobile, probing the often dark air in advance of the body—tell them by detection of odors and by touch what lies ahead of them, for the antennae contain the sense of smell and the most important organs for the sense of touch. Other areas of the ant's body, as the feet and tactile hairs on the body, are also important tactile receptors. The sense of taste is centered in the mouthparts. Like the honeybees the ants receive "sound" as vibrations through solid surfaces; they evidently do not receive airborne sound waves.

Much of the ant's behavior in response to the stimuli she receives is directed by innate responses. These individual responses, which collectively make up complex behavior patterns sometimes referred to as instinct, are present in the ant's brain, inherited from the many generations of ants before her. Thus much of the behavior involved in nest building, eating, and mating is composed of a series of innate responses that are identical for all members of the same age and caste of a single species. These behavior patterns are not learned; the ant is born knowing them.

Ants are not, however, simply robots. It is true that a specific stimulus will often cause a specific response, but above and beyond this level the ant can learn. Within the limitations imposed by the size and development of her brain the ant possesses some rather impressive learning capabilities. Ants are capable of learning by trial and error. For example, they can learn to run a maze with up to six false turns, but if they have learned the route going from nest to food, they must relearn it if the positions are reversed and the sequence is instead from food to nest. Learning also occurs when ants become accustomed to unusual conditions, such as might occur in an artificial nest. This is called habituation. Ants sometimes imitate other ants to a certain degree, and imitation too is a kind of learning. Probably the most advanced type of learning of which ants are capable is memory. Thus an ant may retain a memory of her foraging area—she learns it. She may remember landmarks in the area. She retains a memory of the location of a food source. In fact, the more advanced members of the ant family are even known to retain some memory of a foraging area over the winter.

Ant workers, in contrast to honeybee workers and to the majority of insects, are long-lived. Since worker ants may live two or three years they are able to profit by learning, using what they have learned, such as memory of a foraging area, over a period of time. The colony also benefits by this, since the older workers in certain ways lead the younger, inexperienced workers to food sources that they remember. Ants are not capable of realizing means and ends, cause and effect. They cannot reason. But the wonder of the ants' intelligence is not what they cannot do but rather what they can do with the physical makeup with which they are endowed.

Using their senses, instincts, and learning to respond to conditions about them, how do the ants organize their colonies? Let us look at some of the activities within an ant colony and attempt to dissect their parts.

Temperature regulation within the nest is not developed among the ants to the extent it is among the honeybees. Ant nests are in many cases built so that they provide some temperature regulation. The mounds of ants tend to be warm incubators on sunny days; many nests are built under flat rocks and the upper chambers of these are warmed by the sun shining on the rock. Some *Oecophylla* ants change seasonally from nests on one side of a tree to nests on the other side to obtain optimum temperatures. Some species go deep into the ground to obtain favorable conditions of temperature and humidity. Ants have a delicate temperature sense, as do bees, and the ants shift their brood from place to place to take advantage of different temperatures. Since bees cannot move their young to the temperature needed, as the ants do, they have to create the necessary temperature levels themselves. This the ants need not do, except in so far as placement and construction of their nest is concerned. In the winter when the bees are clustering on their combs, eating their stores, and raising the hive temperature above that of the environment, ants in cold climates are also resting in clusters but they make no attempt to raise the temperature of the nest. Their bodies are able to endure low temperature without freezing and so they spend the winter without either eating food stores (which would be impossible in their stiff, cold condition) or heating their homes. Ants in the tropics, or course, need never adjust to the cold.

In regard to the division of work to be done we find some similarities between ants and honeybees. In both, the queens are the egg layers; the drones' function is but one—to mate with the virgin queens. Among the ants we often find more than one physical form of worker, and this is not true of honeybees. The distinctive soldiers present in some ant colonies largely serve a defensive function. While an ant colony may not have soldiers, it may contain workers of different sizes, and the work done may vary among these sizes, depending on the ants' way of life. Thus among the *Atta,* the leaf-cutters, the very smallest workers stay in the nest caring for the garden and the brood. The medium-sized workers are the foragers, the leaf-cutters. Exactly the reverse situation so far as worker size is concerned has been found with a species of *Formica,* in which the smaller workers do the foraging, in this case for honeydew, and the larger workers collect this from them by regurgitation in the field and in the nest, while also tending to the work inside the nest. This would appear to be a logical adaptation in both cases. In the *Atta* colonies the smallest workers are better able to move about the delicate fungus gardens without breaking them down, while the larger workers are capable of bearing home larger loads than could small workers. In the *Formica* species the smaller ants are nearer the size of the aphids or other homopterans from which honeydew is collected than are the larger workers. It would be logical to hypothesize that they are thus better "milkers," whereas the larger workers would function effectively as "tank trucks," collecting large loads from small deliveries and taking home the supply.

Some ants have a monomorphic worker caste—that is, all workers are of approximately the same size. Among these ants there often appears to be a division of work based on age, and this is certainly a reminder of the honeybee workers. With the honeybees this division is to a large extent dependent upon glandular development. This is not thought to be the case with the ants, at least certainly not to the extent it is in the honeybees. The younger ants tend to stay in the nest for some time after emergence from the pupal stage and become foragers when older. One species of *Myrmica* which was investigated was found to have a division of labor in which the youngest workers cared for the young, the one-year-olds were largely nest builders, and the oldest of the ants were the foragers. A slight correlation between body development and work has been noted for *Formica polyctena*. In this species the workers remained in the nest for slightly over a month, during which time their ovaries became well developed. (This leaves us with some unanswered questions as to how and why these developed.) As this ovary development regressed the workers began to leave the nest and become foragers. Further research may show more such correlations. Some individual ants also tend to show a preference for a certain job and to stay with it indefinitely.

An ant that shows perseverance in a particular job would appear, through this individual trait, to have developed somewhat of a personality of her own. Actually, ants do show individual differences. Just as with the honeybees, some seem to be smarter than others; this has been shown to be true in tests, such as learning a maze. In addition, some ants are known as work-starter or excitement-center ants. These are the members of the colony that appear to the observer to be more intelligent and more excitable than the remainder of the workers. They are often the ones that detect a job to be done, start doing it, and by their activity excite other ants to activity also. They are probably the most venturesome of the foragers. They may well be the individuals who find a new nest site and proceed to move brood and stubborn nest mates by mouth to the new location, the carrying being continued until a large number of the colony members have been convinced and so begin to help in the moving. Among raiding ants it is probably these exciter ants that individually learn the location of a good raiding site and activate and lead the general worker population to it. As with the bees, there are evidently some ant workers which have, in human terms, more individual initiative, and these provide the leaven among the workers. Through the leadership provided by these exciter ants much of the work of the colony is organized, but it is organized simply by their activity and the organization is without orders or forethought.

The ability to differentiate friend and foe is very important for ants. As with bees, the odor of the individual in question is the determining factor. Each species of ant is thought to have a specific odor, although in some ants this may not be well developed. Each colony also has its own nest smell. The two odors combine to provide each colony with its own odor badge by which the members of the colony can readily recognize a nest mate or a "foreign" ant, and for the most part foreigners are immediately considered to be enemies. Several factors may enter into the production of the nest odor—the material of the nest itself, the amount of brood present, waste products, stored food, and other conditions. The main factor, however, appears to be dietary differences between colonies. Most ants are constantly passing food from one to another; included in this food are exudates from the bodies of the queen, the workers, and the brood. The effect achieved by this trophallaxis is to distribute rather evenly among the members of the colony all the various types of food and exudates that are present. In this way all ants are receiving basically the same diet, and their metabolism of this diet provides each with an odor almost identical to that of her sisters. Thus the basis of recognition of friend and foe among the ants is very similar to that of the bees.

The defense measures taken by an ant colony depend to a large extent on the species. Some species of ants if disturbed immediately "play dead"; others take flight. Certain subfamilies, but not all, have stings that inject a venom into adversaries. The most infamous of these ants are the ponerines which we have mentioned as having a potent sting. The venom produced by some of the bull-dog ants has recently been determined to be a proteinaceous venom, closely related to the venom of wasps and bees. Species in some of the other less-advanced subfamilies also have stings. Certainly the *Pogonomyrmex* of the subfamily Myrmicinae have a powerful defense in their stings. Unlike the honeybees, which die after stinging man, ants are not killed but can sting and return another day to sting again.

The mandibles serve as weapons among all the ants. In some species and castes they are of great importance, as in the soldiers of many species, and certainly among the deadly-jawed Amazon ants. A few ants produce from anal glands an odoriferous, irritating secretion which, as it becomes smeared on the bodies of enemies, repels or kills them. Some of the most advanced of the ants, members of the subfamily Formicinae, have lost the sting and instead have in their abdomens a large bladder which contains formic acid. These ants bite their enemies with their mandibles and then from the tip of their abdomen spray the wound with formic acid. Or they may simply squirt the formic acid for a distance of over a foot at things that are disturbing them. They are well supplied with this defense. One investigation revealed that in one species, *Formica rufa,* 19.6 per cent of the body weight may be formic acid.

Ants must be able to orient themselves in order to leave the nest, forage, and then successfully return home. There are three main methods which are used, sometimes singly, oftentimes in combination. We have noted that ants can learn the foraging area by using sight and memory. In this process they learn certain landmarks such as rocks, trees, sandy areas, or other distinctive features of the territory. A young forager ventures out of the nest and learns the immediate area, gradually extending her knowledge outward. Some ants depend to a great extent on this method of orientation.

Like the honeybees, ants make use of sun-compass and polarized-light orientation. In this type of way-finding the ant orients herself by light rays on her outward journey from the nest. On her return trip to the nest she reverses herself, again orienting by light rays. If, however, such an ant is covered and detained in darkness on the outward trail for a few hours, she will, when released, attempt to return home along the trail she followed on the outward journey. The sun, however, will have moved a certain number of degrees in the meantime, and the ant, following the light pattern remembered from her much earlier outward trip, takes a homeward-bound path that would have been correct earlier but is now incorrect by almost exactly the same number of degrees as the sun has moved. She has remembered the pattern to be followed but does not compensate for the passing of time, and so misses home by a certain number of degrees.

The honeybees, as we saw earlier, have such a time sense and are also able to take into account the movement of the sun over a period of time. Experiments such as the one just described indicated that ants lacked this ability of the bees. Recently, however, experimental work showed that apparently some *Formica* workers, which are among the most advanced ants, do have a time sense that allows them to correct for the sun's movement in this type of orientation. Further experiments along this line of inquiry will be extremely interesting. There may be fewer differences in this area between honeybees and at least some ants than was previously thought.

The third means ants may use for finding their way about is odor trails. There are two types of these created by ants. One type, used by army ants, is known as the exploratory trail. As we mentioned earlier, these blind ants hunt in large groups, their success being dependent upon masses of ants staying together in a territory. The army ants as they travel leave glandular secretions to mark their trails. They thus create an odor route for those that follow and also create a means of finding their way back to the colony's bivouac.

The second type of odor trail is known as a recruitment trail, and this type is used by some of the more advanced ants. In this case workers, as they are returning to the nest, mark a trail with glandular secretions from their abdomens, and the purpose of the trail is usually to "recruit" additional workers to the site thus indicated. Such an odor trail may endure only briefly, but if it is marked numerous times by numerous ants, the odor will persist and the path may become a rather permanent road which ants will follow for some distance, and from which they will then branch off in their foraging activities.

An odor recruitment trail left by a worker is a signal to other ants that follow the trail, usually to a source of food. If other workers, in turn, become excited by the find, they also lay down the trail-marking secretion as they return along the trail. Rather recently some exceedingly interesting facts have been learned about these recruitment trails. Dr. E. O. Wilson has found in working with some species that the trail laid by one worker gives four pieces of information in regard to direction and two pieces of information in regard to distance. This amount of information he considers to be roughly equivalent to the amount of direction and distance information communicated in the waggle dance of the honeybee. These recruitment trails may also be used to direct other ants to superior nesting sites; this function is also performed by the honeybees' dances at swarming time.

Honeybees that find a good crop dance and recruit other workers, who in turn return to dance also, to recruit more workers, and so on. It is interesting then to note Dr. Wilson's finding that as ant workers were recruited to a good food source, these additional workers added their scent to the recruitment trail. With increasing amounts of odor substance on the trail, increasing numbers of workers are recruited and still more odor substance is used to mark the trail. Thus a good source is advertised and the better the source the greater the amount of advertising. However, if an ant discovers only a rather poor source of food she may never lay a recruitment trail to it. Even if she does, other ants following may not feel the goal is of sufficient value and will not add their odor substance to the trail. Without reinforcement by other ants the odor substance soon disappears. A poor source would therefore not be well advertised. Thus quite similar types of information seem to be relayed in dissimilar ways, by the honeybees and by some ants.

The glandular recruitment-trail substances studied thus far are specific or separate for each species. The secretions used to lay these trails are pheromones. Other pheromones, such as those we noted that are passed in food, are also present in ant colonies. Only fairly recently have scientists begun the study of these chemicals. We noted when discussing the honeybees that pheromones are probably the most important factor in the organization of the honeybee colony. To that generalization add the ants.

CHAPTER 24

Pheromones in the Ant World

The human body produces hormones, which are of vital significance in ordering the inner workings of that body. Ants, as well as honeybees and termites, produce pheromones, which are of vital significance in ordering the workings of the entire colony. The word pheromones denotes chemical substances which are given off by a living organism, such as an ant or a honeybee, and which, received as an odor or a taste by another organism of the same species, relay a chemical message to the individual, the message often causing a specific response. The use of pheromones by some ants in the laying of odor trails was considered in the preceding chapter.

Pheromones may also be used in some ant colonies to spread an alarm. An excited or alarmed ant may secrete an alarm substance, and this, detected as an odor in the colony, serves to excite other ants. These substances are produced in a variety of ways. In some species the alarm pheromone is produced by the mandibular glands, in others by anal glands, and in some by other glands in the abdomen. The alarm substances are not usually species-specific, as are the trail substances. Alarm can also be spread through a colony by other means, as by excited ants or perhaps also by sound communication received as vibrations.

Other pheromones and exudates present in the colony helping to organize its activities are produced by the larvae and queen. Most ant larvae are carefully and generously fed by their older sisters. They are licked and groomed. If danger threatens the colony the workers take these young, along with the eggs and pupae in the nest, and attempt to move them away from the danger area. The workers' actions appear to be those of maternal solicitude. They are, rather, the actions of self-interested creatures, for from these young the workers derive secretions which they value. It is thought that the larvae of some species when hungry produce chemicals which guide the workers bringing food to their mouths, and it may well be also that pheromones produced by the larvae provide stimuli that induce foraging in the workers which receive them.

That it is secretions, including pheromones produced by the queen, that make her attractive to the rest of the colony, and hence promote her care and protection, rather than her value as an egg layer has been proved. In some species, queen attractants, or queen exudates, were placed on a small piece of wood. About this piece of correct-smelling and correct-tasting wood the workers clustered. They licked it and even transported it as they would a living queen.

Pheromones that are imbibed are gradually passed to the various members of the colony through trophallaxis. The ants are essentially exchanging drops of liquid food from their crops, but mixed in with the food are the pheromones they have received. The process of trophallaxis is more than simply that of an ant feeding a hungry ant, for ants rather constantly carry on trophallaxis whether their crops are full, empty, or in some intermediate condition. As humans might stop to talk to someone and inquire how things are going for him, so ants stop and one gives another a drop of food. By so doing, they too are communicating. Within the drop of food is contained news as to the kind of food the ants in the colony have been eating, the presence or absence of the queen, the presence and status of the brood, the types of guests or parasites present in the nest, and other similar information.

The amount of trophallaxis that is carried on in a colony depends on the species, with the more advanced ants having the highest rates of food exchange. By using radioactive tracers it has been possible to follow the course of food exchange in some colonies. *Pogonomyrmex badius,* a harvester, while not a primitive ant, is not one of the most highly evolved. Food exchange in this colony proved to be very limited. When the tracer element was fed to one worker in a colony of 90 adults, less than 10 percent of the adults had received the introduced material within 11 days. In a more highly evolved ant species, however, a single worker laden with honey mixed with a radioactive isotope of iodine was placed in a colony consisting of 257 adults. Within 4 hours, 40 percent of these had received the tracer material. In 30 hours more than 90 percent had received it!

It had long been thought that no regurgitation and exchange of food whatsoever took place in the most primitive ants, the ponerines. Recent scientific work has, however, proved that regurgitation of food does take place to a certain degree in some of the primitive ponerine genera. As the radioactive-tracer technique has shown among some ant species in other subfamilies, there are all degrees of food and pheromone exchange, depending on the species, and we would hypothesize that the exchange among the ponerines may be on a very limited level. The exchange has been found to be greatest among the most highly evolved ants with the most complex societies; therefore trophallaxis is believed to play a most important part in the organization of the more highly evolved ant societies.

The subfamily Formicinae is considered to include the most highly evolved ants, and the genus *Formica* within this subfamily contains species which sometimes form vast communes or "villages" of ant nests. These ants are considered to be among the most intelligent of the ants, learning readily and displaying adaptability. When radioactive food was introduced into a single nest of one of these ants, it was found that this food was exchanged with ants of the same species from other nests, and these tracer elements traveled up to 200 meters from the nest which was the source.

Research is increasingly indicating that pheromones received by the members of an ant colony either as odors or as imbibed liquids, these latter primarily passed about the colony by trophallaxis, are the great attractants that keep the individual ant in the group, and one of the primary means by which the group's activity is organized. It is neither love nor duty that motivates the ants, but tastes and smells.

By borrowing a clue from the honeybees we are led to wonder whether pheromones play a role in the reproductive cycle of the ant colony. Research tends to support such a view. However, in the area of caste determination the ants present a much more complicated problem than do the bees.

In general, male ants are produced from unfertilized eggs laid by the queen ant or on occasion by unfertilized workers. In this the ants follow the rule established among the honeybees and social wasps. Female ants, both queens and workers, like female honeybees, are produced from fertilized eggs. Since only the eggs laid by the queen ant are fertilized, only these are usually considered to be capable of producing females. However, we noted when discussing the honeybees that occasionally female bees do develop from unfertilized eggs laid by workers and that these exceptional cases occur more often in some races of honeybees than in others. Now it has been learned that in several ant genera workers commonly lay eggs, some of which develop into females. Thus while the general rule of unfertilized eggs equal males and fertilized eggs equal females is true for both the ants and the honeybees, there are known exceptions.

Among the honeybees the presence of the queen discourages or prevents egg laying by the workers. This is generally considered to be true among the ants also, but here again there are exceptions. In several genera, workers are known to lay eggs, some of which may develop, but many of which are eaten. These worker-laid eggs may be fed to larvae that have developed from queen-laid eggs. In some species of *Myrmecia,* a primitive ponerine genus, during the winter eggs are actually solicited from one worker by another and eaten as soon as laid. In *Pogonomyrmex badius* the older queens and young larvae are thought to be fed exclusively with modified worker-laid eggs. (Note that this is the species that showed a low rate of oral food exchange in the experiment with tracers.) There are species of ants in which it has been definitely shown that the presence of the queen inhibits egg production, and this situation is thought to be the more "normal" case, rather than the exceptions just listed. By using queen ants caged by gauze screens in the colonies of some species, it has been shown that actual contact between the queen and at least some of the workers must occur if her influence is to be felt in the colony and egg laying by the workers inhibited. Her odor alone was not sufficient. This would at least appear to indicate a control through chemicals received from her body by the workers by mouth and transmitted to other workers.

If a female ant develops from a fertilized egg, what determines whether that ant will develop into a queen or a worker? On this point we are far from certain. Among the honeybees the determining factor is diet, although all the constituents of that diet are not certain. Among the ants the situation appears to be far more complicated. Of course, in the ants we are dealing with thousands of species which may have developed variations among themselves; in the research done on honeybees we are dealing with but a single main species.

Evidently there are a number of factors that can influence the final outcome of a female ant. In working with species of *Myrmica* it has recently been found that these factors probably include feeding, resting phases, condition of the tending workers, queen influence, bias within the egg, temperatures, and pheromones. This genus lives in areas where cold winters occur, and some of the larvae pass this cold season in the late larval stages in a condition known as diapause, a resting phase. Diapause may also occur under certain other conditions. This resting phase within the larval stage of development is not to be confused with the later pupal stage.

These studies of *Myrmica* showed that if larvae passed through the later larval stage without diapause they became workers. Those larvae which diapaused late in the larval phase might later develop into either queens or workers. Larvae which were very small upon entering diapause developed into workers; large ones might become either queens or workers. If these larvae were placed after diapause in two colonies—one with a queen and one without a queen—more young queens were produced in the queenless colony that in that with an older queen present. In another pair of matched colonies, both without queens, the first colony was given a dead queen each day; the second colony was given a dead worker each day, but no dead queens. The first colony reared 2 queens and 26 workers; the second colony raised 15 queens and 13 workers. The presence or absence of queen pheromones in a colony thus seems to have a part in the determination.

Whether or not a larva enters diapause is partially governed by temperature; larvae in summer when temperatures were higher and more constant often completed their development without any diapause. The workers, however, also exert an influence on the destiny of the egg through their own physical condition, and this condition apparently varies according to the season and temperature.

The eggs laid by the queen may display a bias, it appears, and this may affect their ultimate destiny. In a species of *Formica* the queen in the winter laid a small number of large eggs which usually developed into queens. Her summer eggs were small and developed into workers, but if the small eggs were placed in colonies where there were large numbers of workers present to care for each of the eggs, queens could be produced from them.

Among the ants which have been studied in regard to caste determination, differentiation appears to depend upon many interconnecting factors, among which diet and pheromones are important.

By way of contrast we can cite the case of queen determination in the species *Oecophylla longinoda,* which is unusual in that the workers lay eggs rather freely. In this species the queen lays unfertilized eggs that develop into males and fertilized eggs that develop into workers. The workers lay two sizes of eggs. The larger of these worker eggs become males; the smaller develop into females, either queens or workers. In addition to this rather astounding finding there is some evidence that the true queens themselves never produce queens, but that all young queens develop from worker-produced eggs! This ant is probably an extreme case, but it serves to illustrate that queen determination may vary rather widely among the many species of ants.

Even if we could easily determine what factors influence queen and worker differentiation among the ants, we would still be left with another problem, that of explaining the variations among the workers; as we know, some ants have subcastes of workers, such as the special soldiers.

Here diet may be one of the main controlling factors. One researcher found in working with the genus *Pheidole,* which produces soldiers, that if the larvae were given a diet of sugar-water or honey throughout the larval stage, all became workers. If meat was provided in addition, and given before the fifth day of larval life, these larvae became soldiers.

There is evidence also to suggest that pheromones may play a part here. In two experimental colonies, one with soldiers and one without, more soldiers developed from the brood of the soldierless colony than from the colony already containing soldiers. In fact, in the latter colony soldier production was almost completely lacking.

There is sometimes a wide variation in size among the workers within a colony, and this is thought to be related to the amount of food received by the larvae, the larger workers having received more food in the larval stage. However, ants of the genus *Atta,* which have a wide range of size, tend to confuse this theory, for their young are all fed fungus—even sleep in the fungus—and differential feeding, while it may be possible, would not seem likely here.

We have noted that the first workers produced by many queens who establish colonies on their own are very small—much smaller than future workers will be. This has been considered to result from food shortage. However, eggs of such queens have been placed in thriving colonies of the same species where the eggs and young received optimum care and food, and still only very small workers resulted. This would lead one to believe a bias was present in these eggs, perhaps due to the limited nutritional resources of the queen producing the eggs.

Obviously much remains to be learned about the ants—not only about their caste determination, but also about their pheromones, and their general way of life. Despite the mass of knowledge already compiled, science has barely begun to know what makes ants the way they are. They present an absorbing field of study for those who care to delve into their miniature world.

Part Four

THE TERMITES

CHAPTER 25

Species of Termites

Termites are thin-skinned, soft-bodied, often blind, largely defenseless creatures which are nevertheless highly successful and exceedingly numerous. These creatures are quite different from those we have thus far discussed in our survey of social insects. Whereas wasps, bees, and ants all belong to the highly specialized order Hymenoptera and so are somewhat related, the termites are placed in a completely different, far removed, and more primitive order, the Isoptera, the word Isoptera meaning equal-winged. Termites are the sole members of this order.

Like ants, all termites are social; have castes within the colony; pursue a pedestrian way of life, except for the winged sexuals; live in wood or earth; sometimes build nests; carry on trophallaxis; and certain species harvest food and grow fungus. Ants and termites therefore would appear to be nearly identical, but these common features are deceptive. With the termites we do find social organizations that have some intriguing similarities to those of the ants, but we also find a very distinctive way of life. There are two vital differences between ants and termites. First, in the termite colonies both males and females are present in every caste, including a full-time king, whereas ant colonies have males in the reproductive caste only and these very briefly. Second, termites in their development do not undergo complete metamorphosis, as do the ants and other social insects, but instead pass through an incomplete metamorphosis: egg, nymph, adult.

Many people confuse termites with ants; indeed a common though misleading name for the termite is white ant. The simplest way to differentiate between ants and termites is by the "waist"—the ant's body being constricted into a narrow waist, the termite's not being so constricted. Termites can also be differentiated from ants by the wings: in termites the forewings and hindwings are of equal size; in the ants the forewings are larger. However, most termites and ants seen by the average individual are not the winged forms.

It is the strange ability of termites to use cellulose as a primary item in their diet that has made them a blight and a boon to mankind, although of the two the blight is more commonly emphasized in man's mind. Cellulose, the most durable material formed by plant growth, is resistant to decay and destruction. The termites are not capable of digesting this material on their own; they must have help and help comes in the form of microscopic organisms called protozoa. These creatures live in the intestines of many of the termites and there act upon the wood, breaking it down into substances that the termites can use for their nutrition. In this way the termites provide the protozoa with both board and room, and the protozoa reciprocate by helping the termites with their digestion. This is another example of the situation known as symbiosis in which both participants benefit. Some termites, particularly in the tropics, by consuming great quantities of dead wood help to return its elements to the soil, and they also carry on a vast and constant clean-up campaign. Their paths and those of man often cross, however, and when certain of the termites begin returning the wood of man's homes, fences, and crops to the soil, man vociferously and actively considers termites a blight. As we shall note later, not all termites have their intestinal zoos and not all termites eat wood. Lichens, fungi, grass, and other plant products are also among the substances eaten by certain termites.

The termites lead very secretive lives, enclosing their colonies within protective nests in wood or earth. They are secretive in that the termites themselves are usually hidden, although their nests are sometimes exceedingly obvious, such as the mounds built by some species and the carton nests constructed by others. Inside the nests sufficient humidity is present to keep the termites' soft bodies moist. Since air outside the nest will often dry them quickly and fatally and their fleshy bodies make excellent ant, bird, reptile, mammal, and human food, the termites, with some exceptions, remain within their nests or move to food sources through underground passages or through covered passageways above ground, which they construct to protect themselves.

It is in the tropics that the termites have reached their peak of development, from the standpoint of number of species, number of individuals, variety of nesting habits, and exploitation of the resources of the environment. They are also numerous in the subtropics but become increasingly rare in temperate areas. We find, for example, approximately 50 species of termites in the United States, whereas Africa can boast of nearly 400. Africa has the largest number of species of termites of any area; the Orient places second. In North America four species only extend as far north as southern Canada.

Members of the order Isoptera are divided among six families, five living and one fossil. These families are composed of approximately 2200 species of termites. There are more species of termites than of social bees or social wasps, but fewer than of ants. The most structurally primitive of the five living families of Isoptera is Mastotermitidae, which contains only one living species. The next two families, the Kalotermitidae and Hodotermitidae, are also relatively primitive in structure, but members of the Hodotermitidae have developed some specialized living habits. The Rhinotermitidae is in an intermediate position. The Termitidae is the most advanced family, displaying a wide and interesting array of habits and of nest architecture. The Termitidae family, advanced structurally and socially, is also by far the largest in number of species, containing approximately three-fourths of all the species of termites.

The numbers of individual termites present in a mature colony may vary from a few hundred to a million or more depending upon the species. In general the more structurally primitive termites have small colonies, with the more advanced groups having the larger colonies. An exception is *Mastotermes darwiniensis,* the sole surviving member of the family Mastotermitidae, which, although the most primitive termite alive today, does nevertheless live in rather large colonies.

It comes as no great surprise to find that *M. darwiniensis* is a resident of Australia, home of the primitive ants and mammals. This species betrays the probable origin of the termite group as a cockroach-type creature. In this one species of termite the eggs are not laid singly but instead are cemented together by a secretion into a packet which is highly suggestive of the egg capsule of roaches. The eggs are glued together in two rows and the packet contains 16 to 24 individual eggs. This Australian termite also has a wing structure similar to that of roaches. If we wish to work toward a point of relationship from the other direction, we can find in Australia a primitive roach that breaks off its wings, as do queen ants and the sexual forms of termites. There are even wood-boring roaches known. These subsocial insects live in wood as they eat it, and they digest by means of protozoa in their intestines, as do the more primitive wood-eating termites. The protozoa present in these roaches have been found to be closely related to those which live in the termites' interiors.

From these pieces of evidence the supposition arises that cockroaches and termites both had a wood-eating, protozoa-laden ancestor from which their present-day species were evolved. Cockroaches are among the very oldest known insects. They are thought to have been present on earth 250 million to 300 million years ago, even before the age of reptiles. In 1937 a fossil termite wing identified as being approximately 200 million years of age was discovered in the Ural Mountains. This termite has been scientifically named *Uralotermes permianum* and placed in a sixth family of the Isoptera, the Uralotermitidae. It is the only species included in this family. Other less ancient fossil termites have been found, slightly less than a hundred species. Some of these fossils are classified as belonging to the Mastotermitidae, that family with the sole survivor in Australia. The fossils of this family indicate the presence of these termites during the Mesozoic period, which stretched from about 190 million to 120 million years ago. We cannot pinpoint the age of the termite group with any great degree of certainty, but they are certainly among the most ancient of living things. They are thought to be the oldest of the social groups, their societies considered to antedate even those of the ants.

The ants and the termites present a clear case of convergent evolution. Closely related to the cockroaches, termites have evolved from rather lowly creatures. The ants are considered to have evolved from a more advanced base, that of wasp stock. In spite of their divergent beginnings ants and termites have developed somewhat similar living patterns, both achieving a social way of life. The termites, however, appear to have reached the levels on which we find them today many, many millions of years ago and have largely remained static. Solutions to the problems of living having once been found, they have been retained. The ants have tended to experiment more along the evolutionary path, to develop some odd adjustments to situations, and such anomalies as the slave-making ants have resulted.

CHAPTER 26

Termites and Their Symbiotic Protozoa

Termites are built on the basic insect design—that is, they have three main body parts consisting of head, thorax, and abdomen; six legs; antennae; and a chitinous exoskeleton. Although we shall note exceptions later, in general the chitinous covering of the workers, nymphs, and soldiers is very thin and usually light-colored. The soldiers, however, may have dark, enlarged, heavily chitinized heads that house their weapons, either oversized mandibles or a frontal gland that resembles an elongated nose. These three forms—worker, nymph, and soldier—are usually blind or have only vestiges of eyes. The reproductive forms have eyes, thicker, darkly pigmented exoskeletons, and wings. The physical differences between the castes are thus variations for the duties prescribed for each. The workers, nymphs, and soldiers are the stay-at-homes. Living in complete darkness, they have no need for eyes; living away from sunlight, no need for pigmentation of the body covering; and living in an enclosed humid area, no need for a thick, defensive, chitinous covering. The reproductives, however, must venture out of the protective nest and so they have bodies prepared to endure greater desiccation and light, and wings and eyes to insure their success as travelers in their colonizing flight.

Most termite forms being blind, the senses of taste, smell, and touch are of great importance to them. The antennae as well as numerous sensory pores and hairs scattered over the body act as organs of touch. Termites are also sensitive to vibrations. A sense of taste and possibly also of smell is indicated by the fact that some termites prefer certain types of wood or can be prevented from eating wood if it is treated with certain chemicals. The fact that termites can so effectively eat out large portions of wood, yet maintain the outer shell of the wood, has given rise to the theory that they may have sensory adaptations which are sensitive to the stresses of the wood.

Termite soldiers often strike their heads against the roof and floor of the workings and workers may also strike theirs against the roof. These actions produce sounds. These appear to be a means of communicating alarm or disturbance, being produced as a result of exposure to light, vibrations of the nest, and also sometimes upon encountering other termites. Nest mates receive the vibrations through the substrate by organs on the legs. A termite receiving such vibrations is often moved to strike its head, also producing vibrations.

Termites have a sensitivity to conditions of moisture within their nests and this is vital for the well-being of the colony, which is usually composed of members with thin exoskeletons. Living in the closed environment of the nest allows the termites to maintain the humidity level in their workings at approximately the saturation point. Entrances to the nests are kept closed, and little-used areas may be blocked off through various means of construction to conserve the moisture in the nest. This moisture is derived from the wood or soil that surrounds the chambers, from water in the wood or in other food they eat, and from water formed within their bodies by the metabolism of their food. Different species of termites vary in their water requirements, and it is interesting that some species can live in very dry wood, and others are desert dwellers, yet all manage to obtain sufficient water to maintain saturated or near-saturated moisture conditions within their immediate chambers. The fact that the workings are closed off from the outside air also aids in temperature control. In some types of nests special arrangements are made for ventilation and cooling, and some species shift locations slightly according to temperature variations. For example, a desert species may forage on the surface during the cooler hours, feeding on plants which are under a protective, constructed covering. During the hotter hours they will retire to their cool chambers in the insulating soil.

The termites' mandibles are their tools, and versatile ones they are. They serve to carry building materials, the young (known as nymphs), and food; they may be weapons for killing; they can excavate in soil or wood; they are used in feeding other termites; and these mouthparts that can delicately handle the eggs of the colony can also chew off pieces of hard wood and have been known even to penetrate the lead sheathing on underground cables.

These powerful mandibles are but one in a series of adaptations which allow some (notice we say only some) of the termites to use sound wood as their diet. The small pieces of wood that have been rasped off by the termite's mandibles move through its alimentary canal. This consists of three sections. The foregut includes the crop and terminates in the proventriculus, a muscular organ controlling the movement of the food on into the second section of the canal, the midgut. The third and final section is the hindgut or large intestine. In the crop the bits of wood are stored and compressed awaiting their movement on through the proventriculus, with which the crop merges at its lower end. This proventriculus is composed of a series of structures that grind the wood and allow only the fine, small pieces of wood to be strained through the proventricular valve into the midgut, where secretions are added to the food mass. The hindgut is the section in which the greater part of the digestive process takes place, for here, in those species that have them, live the masses of protozoa on which the termites depend to digest the wood they have swallowed. In these species of termites the hindgut is large, being distended with the collection of microscopic single-celled creatures within it. In one species of termite approximately one-third of the weight of the nymph or young termite was found to be made up of the contents of the digestive tract, which thus included food and living organisms. In the watery realm within the hindgut, protozoa swim, encircle the tiny wood chips, and with enzymes digest the cellulose. From the resulting liquid in the intestine the termite's body absorbs the nutrients it needs. Of the thousands of protozoa present in an individual termite the majority are symbiotes—those involved in the symbiotic relationship—but there are also present some species, known as commensals, that are simply living there but not taking part in the digestive process, and there may be parasitic species. There are also other living things in this thickly populated world, such as fungi and bacteria. Indeed even the protozoa have parasites!

The necessity for the useful symbiotic protozoa in the termites' intestines can be shown by killing the entire contents of a termite's intestine. This can be done by placing a termite in almost pure oxygen under pressure for a specified length of time. The process does not damage the termite but completely annihilates its intestinal boarders. If the termite is not allowed to replace this digestive circus, it will die even though wood is present for it to eat. If, however, it is reinfected with the symbiotic protozoa from others of its species, it will continue to live. This replacement of the protozoan fauna is a normal act, as we shall note when we discuss molting. The symbiotic protozoa within each termite are received from other termites of its species, and so these tiny creatures have been passed through the members of the species for millions of years and have been associated with the termites for so long that they now have singular characteristics which differentiate them from other protozoa. They do, in fact, claim almost a complete order of the phylum Protozoa for themselves. They share this order with only one other group of protozoa and these are none other than the intestinal inmates of the wood-boring cockroaches!

The variety of symbiotic, commensal, and parasitic protozoa and of other organisms present within the wood-eating termites' intestines is remarkably constant within any one species. So distinctive are these groupings of guests that scientists can even use them as an aid toward identification of a termite, certain groups of termites being known as hosts for particular types of microscopic assemblages.

Only about one-fourth of the termite species in the world, however, have these symbiotic intestinal protozoa. Only the more primitive of the termites eat sound wood and thus need this aid in digesting the wood. The more highly developed termites of the largest and most advanced family, Termitidae, do not depend upon protozoa; instead they eat materials other than wood that do not contain such great amounts of cellulose. Their diverse dietary habits we discuss in more detail later.

Undergoing incomplete metamorphosis, the nymph, or young termite, upon emergence is lighter in color and much smaller than the adults but has much the same general body form. With the other social insects this young is a grublike creature, known as a larva and resembling the adults not at all. The termite's growth must be attained in this nymphal stage of life, for once the nymph becomes an adult it will grow no more except in the cases of certain queens. The nymph, however, cannot grow gradually, as the human child does, for it is enclosed in chitinous, nonstretchable armor. It must therefore occasionally shed, or molt, its outer skin and expand in size. At the time of the molt the old skin splits along the top of the nymph's head and thorax. The nymph, with the new exoskeleton underneath not yet hard, expands until it is out of the old skin and emerges as a larger size. The cast-off skin is usually eaten by other termites. The nymph molts on several different occasions and the period between two molts is known as an instar. Although the nymph has the general adult termite body form throughout this growing stage, it may develop certain features as it progresses through the molts—for example, wings, if its destiny is to be a reproductive. In the termites' development by means of incomplete metamorphosis, then, there is no pupal period, or long resting stage, as is present in the Hymenoptera. Growth for the termite young is done by spurts, without the almost magical transformation within the pupal stage that occurs with the ants, bees, and wasps.

The tiny nymphs before their first molt are fed liquid secretions by other members of the colony. As they develop they gradually begin to feed themselves. Conditions in the colony and their own ultimate destiny affect the number of molts they will undergo and the length of time that will be required for them to finish their development. Some never complete it,

Mutual feeding among the termites assumes great importance in the colony organization. Some termite forms cannot, or do not, feed themselves. Above, a worker termite feeds a nasute, the soldier form of certain species. The grotesque, elongated front portion of the nasute's head has a pore through which is released the secretion of the frontal gland. This secretion is squirted at or dropped on enemies and provides a chemical-warfare defense for the termite colony.

being arrested in their development to best serve the purposes of the colony. Others may undergo accelerated development and reach the adult stage as undersized individuals, again depending on the current needs of the colony. Some may begin development toward one caste and because of necessity within the colony undergo gradual changes and emerge as a member of a different caste. Add to this seeming general confusion the fact that both males and females are represented in each of the three castes—reproductive, soldier, and worker. Caste determination is a very complicated process among the termites.

The termites have some of the strangest eating habits on earth. Not only do some of them live on a diet composed largely of splinters, but within the termite colony strange dining habits abound. The workers and the older nymphs often are solely responsible for feeding the king and queen, the young nymphs, and the soldiers. This they do in two different ways. Feeding may be oral, in which case the food is known as stomodeal food, or it may be anal, in which case the food is known as proctodeal. Food may thus move through the alimentary canal of one termite, be passed from the anus to the mouth of another, and yet another. This proctodeal food is a semiliquid, partially digested food. The waste products are often different from proctodeal food, consisting in many cases of rather dry pellets which are discarded or used as a building material for the nest.

Through mutual feeding, the young nymphs of wood-eating species become infected with the protozoa population of the colony, and this population thrives in the nymph's alimentary canal. Then for a period preceding the molt the nymph fasts, the food in its digestive tract is used, and gradually the protozoan population is killed. The linings of the termite's foregut and hindgut are actually invaginations or infoldings continuous with the exterior covering of the termite. Therefore, when the termite sheds its outer covering it also sheds the lining of the foregut and hindgut. The foregut lining does not issue from the mouth but continues on down the alimentary canal, and perhaps some of it is digested along the way. The lining of the hindgut is also voided through the anus. This leaves the nymph not only with a new exterior, but also, except for the midgut, with a clean new inner lining. The protozoa live only within the hind intestine and since these protozoa have been first starved and then cast off, it is necessary for the termite to be reinfected. This happens through mutual feeding, and the acquisition of new protozoa is necessary following each molt.

CHAPTER 27

Termite Cycles and Castes

Termites shun the freedom of the open air and seek the bodily contacts afforded them in masses of individuals crowded into small passageways and chambers. This is true even of the winged reproductive forms, the alates. Then suddenly, when certain conditions prevail, these alates completely reverse their behavior and seek to leave the nests. Even the workers must be touched in some way by this termite madness, for they prepare exits from the nest, which is ordinarily kept tightly closed against the outside environment. The alates swarm out through the openings and fly away to seek mates and sites at which to establish new colonies.

The winged male and female reproductive forms are produced by mature termite colonies. They provide the most usual means by which new colonies are started, although we shall note later two other possibilities for colony foundation. The production of the alates is timed to coincide with favorable swarming conditions. As with the ants, conditions connected with rainfall, temperature, illumination, and season of the year seem to be of prime importance in determining the time for flight, although the conditions required or desired vary considerably among different termite species. Flights often take place during the rainy season or just before the rains begin. Some species fly during the day, others only during late afternoon or early evening. Some fly exclusively at night. The more primitive species sometimes have a rather diffused flight, with individuals leaving the nests on many different occasions over a period of a few weeks or a few months. Among the more advanced species large numbers of alates emerge at one time, and these emergences are synchronized (presumably due to weather conditions) with the emergences of swarms from nearby colonies of the same species. These well-timed swarms allow for cross-fertilization between colonies. Also, since the termites are prey for a large number of animals, the swarms provide vast quantities of individuals at a single time, thus increasing the odds that at least some of the pairs will successfully establish colonies.

The preparations made by the workers for the emergence of these swarms are dependent upon the species. Wood-dwelling workers cut exit holes through to the outside. Earth dwellers may construct long tunnels and covered runways from the nest, opening in favorable locations. More advanced species may even build certain special structures from which the alates take flight. Soldiers guard the exits from the nests and workers often mill about just inside or outside these openings. The alates often fly out in vast numbers, particularly in the tropics, where at night they may be drawn to man's lights in disturbing quantities. Once the alates have flown, the workers of the parent colonies quickly close the openings in the nests and life therein settles back to dark normality.

The winged males and females fly away from the nest and may be aided by air currents in their travels. Usually none travels any great distance. The more primitive species tend to be the stronger fliers, with more advanced species displaying a weaker, fluttering, less effective flying ability. Among the ants the flight of reproductives is a nuptial flight, mating taking place at the time of the flight. With the termites it is known as a dispersal or colonizing flight, for mating does not take place immediately but occurs later, after the home has been established.

The winged termite males and females alight after flying about, and then with most species dealation, or dropping off of the wings, occurs. These wings have a line of weakness, or suture, near the base, along which they break. With some species, usually the more advanced, the break is made easily; with others, usually the more primitive species, the suture is not so well defined and the termites must rub and pry their wings against objects to cause them to fall off. Just before or after dealation, males and females are attracted to each other and pairing occurs.

The individual termites move about on the ground until a member of the opposite sex is found. The female displays a characteristic behavior pattern consisting of excited movements with the tip of her abdomen elevated. The males are attracted, evidently by this behavior and probably by the female's emission of a scent. The male falls in line behind the female and follows her in her scurryings about in search of a nesting site.

Among some of the more primitive termites the wings are not lost until after pairs have formed and are enclosed within the new colony site. One species has been reported in which the winged female, as she alights, is carrying the already dealated male on her back. In another species, a member of either sex, after having lost the wings, will search for a nesting site and having found one, will move in. While living alone the termite, whether male or female, leaves the tip of its abdomen outside the nest opening, thereby attracting a member of the opposite sex. The waiting may be lengthy, up to several weeks. However, these are exceptions to the general pattern of termite colony foundation, which normally consists of flight, dealation, pairing, site seeking, and closure within a cell, followed by mating.

As though suddenly regaining their proper termite senses, the dealates, as they are called after having lost their wings, following their pairing quickly revert from being drawn to light to being repelled by it. Each couple seeks a proper nesting site and, depending on their pattern of living, prepares and enters a cell in either wood or soil. Within this they seal themselves. After all these preparations have been completed—often several days' worth—mating finally takes place. Copulation will be repeated from time to time throughout the lives of the king and queen. Here a most obvious difference between Hymenoptera and Isoptera appears—the termite male reproductive is not doomed to early death as are the male wasps, bees, and ants. Instead the male termite, now known as the king, remains with the female, the queen, and reinseminates her from time to time.

Among the lower termites, life within the cells moves at a gradual pace. In one species of the genus *Reticulitermes* it was found that the queen laid no eggs at all for the first 40 days following mating. After 150 days only about a dozen had been laid and approximately 50 days was required before the nymphs were produced. The reproductives in these lower species feed on material available to them in their nest and so are not forced hurriedly to develop nymphs to obtain food for them. The higher termites, however, often nest in the soil, where for some their food is not readily available; therefore speed in producing workers is important. These more advanced reproductives, like the ant queens, have a supply of nutritive material within their bodies to sustain themselves and the first young. Mating, egg laying, and development of the young take place much more rapidly in these termites than in the more primitive species. The king and queen care for the first brood, feeding them until they are developed

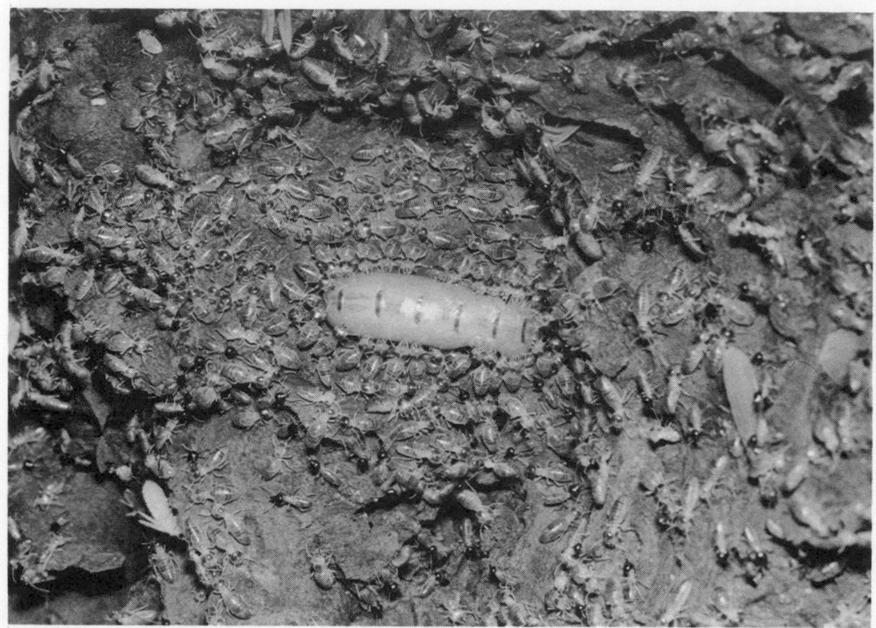

Breaking open a carton termite nest and carefully searching through its pieces, the photographer located the queen near the center of the nest. The queen is exceedingly popular with the members of her colony due to the body exudates she produces, and they cluster about her. The queen's huge white abdomen is greatly distended with eggs. Her head, to the right of the abdomen, is covered by the attending workers. The nasutes, or soldiers, of this colony, with their dark elongated heads, are also present in the picture.

sufficiently to feed themselves. The young thus produced gradually take over the household chores, now feeding their parents and freeing them for their reproductive roles, and thus the colony is established.

Depending on the species, once a colony is mature, the queen's egg-laying rate may reach enormous proportions—as may the queen. One tropical queen is reported to have laid 86,400 eggs in a day! Abdomens of the queens usually become somewhat distended, but in some species the enlargement of an older queen is tremendous. Such queens are said to be physogastric; their enlargement does not involve a molt. The largest termite queens are those of the African genus *Macrotermes*. These queens develop abdomens so distended with eggs that their bodies may ultimately be almost 5 inches in length, over 1 inch in width, and 1 inch in height. Their consorts are only slightly more than ½ inch in length and stand ⅛ inch tall. Such gigantic queens are thus reported as being approximately 160 times the size of the king by volume, and 2400 times the size of the workers. The distended abdomens of such queens, like those of the honey-pot ants, have the abdominal sclerites pulled far apart. The intersegmental membrane of the abdomen reveals a creamy, egg-white color on the termites and a golden-honey color on the ants—both distended, but for different purposes.

The body form developed by young will ultimately place them in one of the castes of the termite colony. In the lower termites, young nymphs through the first two to three instars are much alike except for size, and their ultimate caste destination is often not determined or obvious at this

The head and antennae of this queen termite can be seen to the left of her light-colored, distended abdomen. This particular queen, photographed in Mexico, measured 1¼ inches in length. She is many times larger than any other individual in her colony. Some African queens may become so distended that they are four to five inches in length, and in volume are two thousand times as large as their workers.

point. In the higher termites caste determination often takes place much earlier, evidently during the first instar in some species. As the nymphs move through successive molts, varying features develop, as wings on those developing into sexual forms. The ants, bees, and wasps depend upon the adult females of the species to carry out the work of the colony. The termites not only depend upon the females but also use males on all levels, and then go even further by using child labor of both sexes. By the third instar the nymphs in the lower termites and also in some of the higher species participate actively in the jobs that must be done in the colony, such as caring for the eggs, tending the young, building or excavating the nest, and feeding the king, queen, soldiers, and youngest nymphs.

In some of the more advanced termites there is a definite worker caste. These workers are wingless individuals, similar in appearance to the nymphs. They may reach their full development after only the second or third molt, especially in young colonies where they are needed immediately, or under more favorable circumstances may undergo more molts and reach a larger final size. Workers may be present in a colony in as many as three varying forms, these variations sometimes being in structure and sometimes simply in size. These true workers are evidently little more than nymphs that have been arrested in their development, are in a terminal form, and cannot progress to become members of any other caste. Some of these terminal worker forms, however, do display some distinct characteristics not present in the nymph.

The most primitive termites, of the families Mastotermitidae and Kalotermitidae, do not produce a worker caste. Instead all the work is done by the nymphs. These nymphs can and under certain conditions do continue their development and ultimately become soldiers or reproductives. However, many of the nymphs simply reach a certain point and do not continue their development, or more likely are prevented from continuing it, unless a need is felt in the colony. Individuals such as these, which can continue their development (unlike the true terminal workers in other species which cannot) but nevertheless tend to remain static at a nonterminal stage, are called pseudergates, or false workers. They provide a working force and also double as a reserve that can be called upon when the colony finds itself in need of soldiers or reproductives.

The soldiers represent yet another termite caste; this caste is thought to be a more ancient development with the termites than the worker caste. Whereas a good many genera of termites have no worker caste there is only one genus which lacks soldiers. It is thought that at one time this genus also had soldiers but has since lost them. The termite workers and nymphs are relatively helpless—their bodies are soft; they lack a sting; and the mandibles while effective for the work the termite does, are not warrior's weapons. To the soldier caste falls the duty of defending the colony, and the soldiers' heads are modified for their jobs. There are two main types of soldiers. In one the mandibles have been developed as defensive weapons. These soldiers have enlarged, heavily chitinized, and pigmented heads and mandibles. The mandibles have been modified in various ways. The soldiers in some species have very large, heavy, chopping mandibles; others have slender, pointed ones for piercing an enemy; and in some the mandibles are twisted and are believed to snap foes away. When a breach in the colony's covering has been made, the soldiers fill in the gap, acting as defenders as the workers repair the damage to the walls. Just as with some of the ants, the powder-post termites have soldiers with heads especially modified to plug the colony's narrow runways, thus filling a defensive role.

The second type of soldier is one that depends upon chemicals to conduct its warfare. These soldiers have a greatly developed frontal gland located in the head. Produced in this gland is a chemical which when squirted or dropped on an enemy entangles it and/or causes chemical injuries to it. The opening from the gland in the center of the head is a pore called the fontanel. In some species this pore occurs just above the mouth and secretes a sticky substance that is rubbed off onto the enemy, causing it to become entangled. In other species there is a groove down the front of the head; the material runs down this, gets on the termite's mouthparts, and is then spread on the enemy. The most extreme form of these soldiers has the front of the head pulled out into a long, sharp point, in the tip of which occurs the pore through which the material issues in long, sticky threads. In these threads the termite's attacker becomes entangled. These soldiers are fittingly called nasutes in reference to their strange snouts (*nasus* being Latin for nose). Their mandibles are greatly reduced. One tropical American termite genus includes some species that have in their colonies two forms of soldiers. The larger type has heavy mandibles, frontal tube, and also, on the upper lip, a trough through which flows a toxic secretion. The smaller soldier has small mandibles, an elongated frontal tube, and grooved upper mouthparts for chemical warfare.

Probably most or all of the soldiers are fed by workers or nymphs, their strange mandibles or stranger "noses" making it difficult or impossible for them to feed themselves. In this we are reminded of the Amazon ants with their formidable jaws. The enlarged heads of the termite soldiers are no indication of their brain power. In the one type of soldier the large head mainly houses muscles to move the big mandibles. In the other type, the space is filled with the large frontal gland, source of the chemical secretion. In some of the species this gland may even extend back from the head and fill up a portion of the abdomen also.

Once a termite colony has attained a certain size and stability many of the nymphs, at certain times of the year, complete their development into alates and these eventually leave the colony to establish additional colonies of the species. As an indication of the long life of individual termites and the slow rate of their development, almost a year may be required among the higher termites for the development of an alate from the egg to adult. In some of the lower termites two years may be required for the same process.

In some colonies, depending on the species and the need, additional reproductive forms may develop. The primary reproductives, the founding king and queen of the colony, often remain as the single reproductives among their thousands of offspring for many years. If anything happens to one or both of these the colony would seem to be doomed. But this is not usually the case, for the colony produces what are known as second-class reproductives. These are either males or females, or both, in answer to the needs of the colony. They develop from brachypterous nymphs (having wings or the beginning of wings) already present in the colony. These supplementary reproductives do not have the long wings which characterize the primary reproductives, although they have wing pads. They have less well-developed compound eyes and are less darkly pigmented than the primary forms. In some species at least, the second-class female reproductives tend to produce more eggs than did the original queen. Although the primary king is monogamous in so far as the primary queen is concerned, at her death he may obtain a harem of more than a dozen of the second-class queens. Even a third-class reproductive form may occasionally be present. This is a supplementary reproductive which has developed from an apterous nymph (without wings or beginnings of wings). Occasionally a supplementary reproductive will develop from a nymph that has just started differentiation into a soldier. In this case the reproductive will have a head that is soldierlike. In the case of the highest termite family, Termitidae, the supplementary reproductives are usually developed from brachypterous nymphs. It is in this family that differentiation of the nymphs occurs at an early stage of development.

Those species that live in wood or soil and gradually spread out in many directions as their population and activities increase may develop groups of workers, soldiers, and nymphs that have only limited contact with the king, queen, and main body of the colony. In these outlying areas, oftentimes secondary reproductives will develop from nymphs and come to reign over these now-separate kingdoms. This is a second means of colony formation, known as budding, the first means being, of course, by a primary king and queen. The presence of these secondary reproductives as heads of "budded" states is more common among the primitive families.

A third method of colony founding has been described, in which a colony divides by fission. That is, a group of all castes and ages leaves the old site and moves to another, where a new colony is established either with the original king and queen or with supplementary reproductives. This method has been hypothesized from a relatively few observations of such incidents, when the usually negatively phototropic termites were seen moving in daylight. There is a possibility that these moves were undertaken to escape army ants, rather than to found a new colony.

From the nymphs present within a termite colony, individuals to fill caste positions are produced as they are needed. If supplementary reproductives are needed they develop; if additional soldiers are needed, they too develop. Nymphs can undergo developmental molts, eventually becoming terminal workers, soldiers, supplementary reproductives, or alates; they can be arrested at a given point and remain there indefinitely as pseudergates; or they can even regress in their development—that is, a nymph showing signs of wings may at a following molt return to winglessness. These generalizations are primarily true of the more primitive termites. Members of the Termitidae tend to show more differentiation of the nymph at much earlier stages; an individual destined to be an alate is often obvious after the first molt and its development does not then regress to a lower caste.

Pheromones are thought to have a great deal to do with caste differentiation among the termites, although this is an extremely complicated matter. Certainly trophallaxis plays an exceedingly important part in the life of the termites. The king and queen, soldiers, and youngest nymphs are fed by the workers, and the workers trade food back and forth. Among the colony members there is a constant exchange of food both orally and by transfer from anus to mouth. Mutual grooming is a rather constant activity, one termite cleaning and grooming another with its mouthparts. In this regard the queen is particularly popular, being constantly surrounded by colony members who groom and lick her, presumably receiving tasty body exudates. The termites would thus appear to have a way of life admirably suited for pheromonal control of castes.

The presence of a pair of primary reproductives is known to inhibit the development of secondary reproductives in a colony. Experimentally, if a queen termite is placed in a screen so that her head is in one group of termites and her abdomen in another, the production of supplementary reproductives is completely inhibited only in the colony in possession of her abdomen (provided a king is present in this colony also). The theory is that the pheromone or pheromones causing this inhibition may be passed through the queen's intestine and, in the form of proctodeal food provided by the queen, eaten by the nymphs or workers and passed on to others in the colony in the same way. If, instead, a nymph is placed in the screen, its head in a colony with a queen, its abdomen in a colony without a queen, the latter colony is still prevented from producing supplementary reproductives, evidently by pheromones received through the imprisoned nymph. It is interesting that in these cases kings also must be present with the queens. Complete inhibition of supplementary reproductives occurs only when both individuals are present—the pheromones from the two must be available together.

The production of soldiers appears to be inhibited by the presence of other soldiers. In some cases a young colony may have only a single soldier. Until the colony attains a larger size no additional ones are produced. If this single soldier is taken away another one is usually produced. The number of soldiers produced is based on a ratio of the number of soldiers to nonsoldiers. As additional nonsoldiers are produced a limited number of soldiers is also produced to maintain the ratio. It is thought that a soldier can be developed from any nymph still capable of molting. Such a nymph enters a soldier-nymph instar, finally molting to become a true soldier.

In working with a rather primitive termite, results showed that a nymph might go through five to eight molts and remain a pseudergate, or it could undergo development into a supplementary reproductive, a presoldier, or a first-stage nymph. This first-stage nymph could then molt to a presoldier, a supplementary reproductive, or a second-stage nymph, or could regress to a pseudergate. And finally the second-stage nymph could develop into any of the stages listed for the first-stage form, or even to an alate. The soldier, true-worker, alate, and supplementary-reproductive forms, once reached, are permanent. At least with this one species the further development and differentiation of the pseudergates appear to be inhibited by the presence of terminal forms within the colony, but once the inhibitions are removed, the nymphs' development may take any of a wide range of directions.

It has recently been found with this species that when an inhibition is removed only pseudergates that have recently molted are capable of taking advantage of the change and continuing their development. Once these have developed into terminal forms they in turn inhibit the development of others.

Pheromones are rather widely thought to be, and partially proven to be, the primary factors organizing the caste system of the termites. This theory is far from being completely tested for most species. The more advanced termites present additional problems, and further study of caste determination in these will no doubt provide some interesting discoveries.

Work done on soldiers serves to demonstrate the complexity of the caste problem in termites. In many species more than one size of soldier is present. This may in some cases be due to the length of the developmental periods, the soldiers developing from two or even three different instars. In some species there may be two distinct body forms present among the soldiers, as those we mentioned earlier. In some experimental work this dimorphism has been found to be tied in with the sex of the individual. For example, in working with one species it was found that the smaller workers were males and the larger workers were females, but even among the small male workers and the large female workers there was size variation, resulting from development from different instars. In this same species the soldiers were usually females. In other species different combinations of size, sex, and form were found.

In the genus *Zootermopsis* soldiers of various sizes, depending on the instars from which they developed, were produced in one series of experiments. This production was a concentrated affair and the members of the colony controlled the final number produced by eating a portion of the soldier crop, consuming primarily the smaller soldiers.

Caste determination among the termites is a fertile field for research. Although we are far from knowing exactly how it is achieved, we do know that the termites have developed highly successful organizations, their strength based on the use of the individual for the good of the whole. Even the ultimate destiny in body form for each individual is completely dependent upon the needs of the colony. It is an efficient but grim solution to the problems of living.

CHAPTER 28

Termite Homes and Foods

With many termites home and food are practically synonymous. Some eat away at their homes; others at least partially construct their homes from fecal wastes, the remains of their food. Termites can be divided into two main groups on the basis of location—they are either wood dwellers or earth dwellers. Termites can also be categorized according to their food habits. And, finally, if they construct distinctive homes, which many of them do, they can be divided into general types on this basis also.

Some termites which survive on a diet of wood are found living within that wood, without any connections between their homes and the soil. These include damp-wood species, dry-wood species, and some known as powder-post termites. Wood dwellers are among the most primitive termites. They do not construct any type of nest but simply live in the excavations they have made in the wood they are eating. The king and queen in establishing the colony select a proper site, excavate a small cell, seal themselves in, and slowly reproduce. After a number of years the colony may reach the size of several hundred to a few thousand individuals, who have, through their appetites, hollowed out the area in which they are living. Additional colonies may spring up about this original one by budding. All of the wood-dwelling termites are dependent upon their internal protozoa to digest the wood they eat. Fungus growth is often present on the walls of the cavities made by wood-dwelling species. This growth may act as an aid in breaking down the wood even before it is ingested by the termites, and it is thought that the fungus itself may also provide a small but important part of the diet of the termites.

Damp-wood termites require a great deal of moisture and so are commonly found in rotting trees. The groups of termites which choose dry, sound wood rather than damp, rotting wood in which to dwell are known as dry-wood termites. This wood may be in the form of dead trees or parts of trees, poles, and buildings. The most extreme of the dry-wood termites are the powder-post termites. These do not need connections to the ground and are capable of living in very dry wood; therefore they can live inside houses in the woodwork and even in furniture. Their fecal pellets, found inside their workings or dumped out of their living quarters onto the floor, are small and extremely dry, reflecting the dry wood on which they feed, hence the name powder-post. These termites have soldiers with heads specialized to act as "plugs" in the narrow runways as a defensive measure.

There is another large group of termites that also eat sound wood but live in the earth or at least usually maintain contact with the soil through constructed runways. These belong to the earth-dwelling classification. One group, known as subterranean termites, includes those that do not build exposed nests on the surface of the ground. Their contact with the earth is a provision for a necessary moisture supply which they derive from the soil. The subterranean termites, like the wood-dwelling ones, have symbiotic intestinal protozoa that help to digest the cellulose the termites eat. Included in this subterranean group are some of the most infamous species of termites, for certain of these cause great economic loss.

Among the subterranean termites the king and queen in founding a colony prepare a cell either in the earth or in moist wood located in or on the soil. As the colony develops, the members excavate passageways through the wood, maintaining their soil connections, or they excavate passageways through the soil and attack wood from below through their tunnels. When these termites locate wood that is separated from the soil by a barrier, such as a cement foundation, they will build covered runways over the offending material, connecting the soil to the wood source. Through these passageways the termites do their traveling, safe from small predators and drying air. These tubes may be constructed upright to a source, or may be suspended downward from heights. They are built from grains of sand, soil, or wood, glued in place with liquid from the mouth. Soldiers stand guard at the mouth of a runway as it is being constructed. The construction is carried on from within the tube, the workers bringing bits of material through the already completed tube, placing them, and then returning through the tube for more material.

A well-known example of such a subterranean termite is one known as *Reticulitermes hesperus*. Its colonies are established within a small cell in the earth or in wood in contact with the soil. Mating follows shortly after the two reproductives seal themselves in the cell with bits of wood and fecal matter. Less than a dozen eggs are produced in the first group and these are laid several days apart. The eggs, which are cleaned and cared for by the king and queen, require from 30 to 100 days of development before the young hatch. These are either fed by the parents orally or may take food from the anus of the parents or later nibble at fecal wastes in the nest. The initial growth of the colony is very slow, but eventually workers and soldiers are produced in increasing numbers. Finally alates will be produced, but not until the colony is at least three or four years old. The individual termites are long-lived, probably reaching an age of three or four years; kings and queens will live longer. The gradual increase of the colony population, coupled with the queen's increasing ability to produce large numbers of eggs, eventually produces a colony that may contain several hundred thousand members. The primary reproductives are replaced by supplementaries if some disaster occurs, and probably supplementary forms arise on the fringes of the colony after it has achieved a large size. These supplementary queens are very productive; it is reported that a secondary queen of this species may lay as many eggs in one day as a primary queen produces in the first two years of colony founding.

A number of factors obviously contribute to the success of this species. Its food is readily available and need not be shared with many other creatures. Its nests are not extensive affairs but are mainly tunnels through soil and wood, and the colony can always shift slightly to a better nearby food source, tunneling as it goes. The queen is not exceedingly distended, and she and the king can move from one gallery to another as temperature or other conditions make such moves advisable. Since the colony stays in contact with the ground, the need for moisture is met. The covered passageways provide a valuable extension of the range the termites can cover, and the nest in the soil provides protection. The king and queen are potentially long-lived, but if anything does happen to them they can be replaced by equally fertile, or even more fertile, supplementary reproductives. The workers, too, have long lives for insects. It is obvious that *R. hesperus* has settled on a successful formula for living.

We have been discussing termites which eat primarily sound wood and are aided in their digestion by distinctive protozoa. Let us now look at some of the more diverse dietary habits displayed by other members of the termite group, all of whom lack these wood-digesting microorganisms. Although some of these species may have protozoa present in their intestinal tract, these are not of the correct type for digestion of wood. Termites without symbiotic protozoa constitute the majority of termite species. They consume plant materials that contain less cellulose than sound wood, or food in which the cellulose has already been partially broken down. Included among the food resources of various species of these more advanced termites are such materials as fungus, grass, leaf mold, decayed wood, weathered wood, vegetable debris, dry manure, humus, algae, and lichens.

An interesting group of termites has adjusted to life in the dry desert. They obtain sufficient moisture for survival by nesting deep within the soil. These species build earthen tubes or flat sheaths around vegetation on the surface of the ground, sometimes completely enclosing each individual stem and branch of small plants, or covering large patches of bigger plants. Within this protective covering the termites eat away the outer layers of the vegetation. In walking through the desert one may find what appear to be small earthen plants, the soil of which they are composed faithfully duplicating each stem and branch of the original plant. Breaking these open, one may find the interior empty, the real plant having been eaten completely away, or only the coarser, tougher parts of the plant may remain. Where larger plants, such as the ocotillo or the saguaro cactus, have covered areas, in these areas the plants' outer layers will be stripped away. In some cases the vegetation attacked may be dead; in other cases it is living. Since these termites do not have symbiotic protozoa, either they are capable of digesting this material, which may be weathered, or possibly, as has been suggested, within the covering tubes fungi may develop on the vegetation, making the plant material available as food. The fungi themselves may serve as a source of food.

Some termites, instead of staying hidden in their protective nests, actually leave these in broad daylight, move across the surface of the ground without protecting passageways, and forage for food, which they bring back to the nest. These are the harvesters of the family Hodotermitidae. In contrast to most termite workers, those that forage in the open are not the usual pulpy white but are darkly pigmented. They have a more heavily chitinized body and are not blind, but have functional compound eyes. These harvester workers move out in files from the nest, much like ants.

They return with pieces of grass which are stored in chambers in their underground nests. It may be that within the humid, warm nests bacteria attack the grass stores, partially decomposing them. While these harvesters are considered to be primitive structurally, they have nevertheless developed a specialized way of life. This harvesting habit is also found in the subfamily Nasutitermitinae of the highly evolved Termitidae. In these species the foragers are accompanied by their specialized, chemical-producing soldiers as a defensive measure. These species collect grass and leaves which are stored in the nest.

Some species of Termitidae are reported to forage freely on the surface at night for lichens and algae; they may also gather some wood. These materials are rolled into pellets which are taken back and stored in the nest. There appears to be a division of labor between the smaller and larger workers among these foragers. They too are accompanied by soldiers.

The humus contained in top soil is the main source of food for certain termites. These soil-feeding termites ingest large quantities of soil, digest the humus from it, and excrete the remainder, which serves them as a valuable building material.

Among the most striking of the termites of the world are those that grow fungus as a part of their food supply. Some of these construct very large mounds in parts of Africa, have colonies reaching enormous sizes, and in certain cases have very large queens. We are reminded of the ants of the genus *Atta,* which also grow fungus, develop colonies of enormous sizes, have large queens capable of independent colony founding, and although they do not build structures above ground as some of the termites do, do develop vast underground nests.

The fungus-growing termites are all found within the subfamily Macrotermitinae of the family Termitidae. Some species dwell only in underground nests; others extend their subterranean quarters by building mounds above them. The workers collect various plant materials, such as grass, leaves, and dry wood. These serve as food, although much of the material probably passes through the termites' bodies without being completely digested. The excrement and other materials, such as chewed wood and clay, are used to build up a base upon which fungus is grown in various chambers of the nest. The design of the fungus combs varies among the different species, some being described as walnut size, others as the size of a man's head, and some as resembling corals or sponges. As with the fungus-growing ants, these fungi do not produce the fruiting body, the mushroom, but do produce bromatia, which is the part on which the termites feed. It appears, however, that this fungus food is used only for the young and the fertile forms. In this respect the termites show far less dependence upon their crop than do the *Atta,* in which the whole colony is totally dependent upon the fungus for their food supply.

Turning now from food to homes, we find that the simplest termite homes are those belonging to the dry-wood, damp-wood, and powder-post termites, which live in the chambers they have eaten out of wood. Yet these homes are not so simple when one considers that the termites honeycomb or hollow out the center of the wood and yet keep the exterior intact. They make exits to the outside through the wooden walls for the flight of the alates or to remove fecal pellets from the nest, but these are made for a purpose and then immediately filled in.

Slightly more advanced types live in chambers in the soil, with tunnels radiating out from these to tap sources of food. Some species, rather than using random workings, actually construct walled, subterranean nests out

Carton nests constructed by termite colonies are distinctive features of tropical landscapes. These are built around branches high in the trees or may be placed in other locations, such as around fence posts. The termites move from the nest to other areas—to the ground, for example—through constructed enclosing passageways. Pictured is a carton nest in Yucatan.

of such materials as earth, sand, saliva, plant particles, and fecal materials, used in varying combinations and amounts. In some species that have such constructed underground nests the colony may occupy a series of them connected by passageways. Others may have such underground nests surrounded by an air space. In one genus such a nest surrounded by an air space has special structures with small pores, evidently to allow air exchange between the nest and the area surrounding it.

The tropics are characterized by strange and obvious termite nests, or termitaria, which occur above ground. These may be in trees or may consist of mounds on the surface of the ground. The primary reproductives of the species that build such nests establish themselves in cells in the earth. Their progeny, in time, may build these outstanding nests, and the reproductives may then be found in these upper portions of the nest. It is thought that contact with the soil is always maintained. From arboreal nests, the contact is through covered passageways back to the soil. The mounds are built over an underground portion of the nest.

Some termites, like some ants, make a material known as carton. The termites derive this paperlike substance from fecal materials containing

When the interior of a carton termite nest is exposed by removal of the outer layers of the nest, the thousands of tiny inhabitants scurry about through the myriad passageways in excitement. To the termites—light-colored, relatively soft-bodied, largely defenseless, and accustomed to living in darkness—the nest is their protection, and damage to it spells disaster for large numbers of individuals.

small undigested bits of wood, mixed sometimes with more wood fragments, earth, and saliva. Out of this papier-maché some termites build large globular aerial homes which are attached to posts or trees. They may be several feet in diameter and are made up of innumerable passageways separated by thin carton walls or have an interior arrangement of horizontal chambers connected by passageways. Through these passages thousands of termites move in busy and unbelievably crowded activity. Constructed runways lead to the ground and to areas where the termites may obtain food. Carton nests may also be built underground, and in this location more earthen materials may be added to the outer layers.

Some species of termites build extraordinary mounds rising as high as 30 feet. The structures of other species are far less spectacular, but all are amazing when one considers that these are the constructions of blind insects less than an inch in length. Depending upon the species building them and the soil and weather conditions where they are constructed, these mounds may vary from rounded mounds to those that assume a tall, single-chimney form to those that sport several turrets. They vary in height from 1 to 30 or more feet, and some of the lower ones have sufficient girth to support the growth of trees on top of them.

Those termites that use humus as their diet and eat a great deal of soil in order to obtain it have an excellent building material in their waste products. This material is molded into a nest structure composed of cells surrounded by a hard outer layer, which may be entirely subterranean or may extend above ground as a usually low mound. Some types of termites which do not feed on the soil nevertheless construct mounds by carrying bits of sand and subsoil from the subterranean portions of the nest and gluing these in place with various secretions. The most spectacular mounds built in this manner are made by African fungus-growing termites. Their nests vary somewhat, but a large mound nest of such fungus growers may basically resemble a hard clay hill 15 or more feet across at the base and approximately the same height. From the peak down the sides of the nest are projecting ridges. Inside this mound the living quarters are near the center. Included here is a cell for the king and queen, the queen now grown so large that she cannot move out of the surrounding cell through the smaller passageways. Fungus gardens are found in many chambers. A million termites may inhabit the various rooms and passageways. Below the central living area is a hollow space or "basement," and another hollow, the "attic," is above the living quarters. The outer walls enclosing this populous city are very heavy.

In order for this million or so inhabitants to live within the mound, some form of air exchange must be, and is, practiced. Air warmed by the termites' bodies and by the growing fungus gardens rises through the nest and flows into the "attic." From there it is funneled outward through a series of ducts into the thick walls. The pressure created by more heated air following it causes the air to continue moving. The ducts ramify into increasingly smaller passageways which finally channel the air along the thin walls of the outer projecting ridges of the nest. As the air flows downward just inside the walls of these projecting ridges, carbon dioxide is lost through the walls to the outside atmosphere, and oxygen is picked up. The purified air is then channeled through the continuing duct work into the "basement," and so the cycle begins again.

Australia, the center for the unusual in animal life, has a termite species which constructs some of the strangest of insect structures. *Amitermes meriodionalis,* the compass termite, builds earthen mounds that may be

These impressive earthen mounds are constructed by termites in Australia, and some of the mounds may be eighteen feet in height. The material from which they are constructed becomes extremely hard, almost like concrete. The species building these large mounds are small in body size, but large in colony numbers.

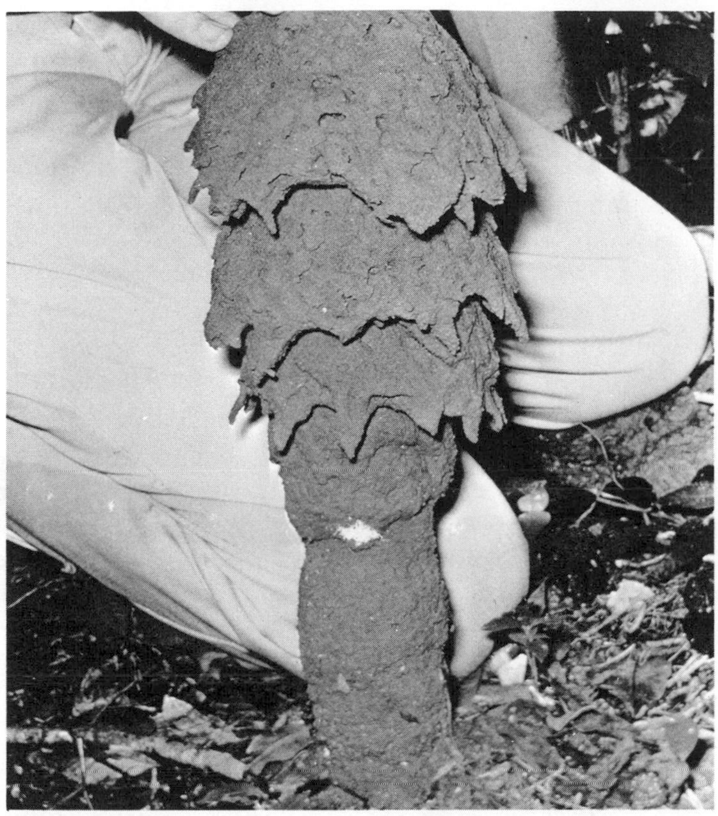

Earthen termite nests assume many varying forms depending on the species building them. The umbrella-topped nest is constructed in this particular manner presumably to shed water. It was photographed in the rain forest of Liberia.

approximately 12 feet high and 10 feet long but are only 3 to 4 feet wide. They are wedge-shaped and the axis of the mound always points north and south. It is conjectured that this placement aids in temperature control, the heat at midday striking only the point of the wedge. These giant mounds are not built for growing fungus, however, as Australia has no fungus-growers.

The internal structure of a nest and the method used in building it remain constant for a species, but environmental conditions may cause the ultimate result to vary either in form or in size in different areas. Also, the location of the nest may vary depending upon the environment. A species which usually constructs an arboreal carton nest may under particular conditions shift to building the same type of nest underground.

Limited though their resources are, different groups of termites have developed a large number of types of building materials. Some of these dry to cementlike hardness, and dynamite may be required to remove the mounds. Some species cement sand grains together, using clay and saliva. Others are masons, using moldable, claylike excreta; by some earth, saliva, and fluid fecal matter are combined; others plaster inside walls with fecal material only; wood, saliva, and fecal carton are another combination. Not only nests but also other structures are built from these and other strange combinations. Of these the above-ground passageways are the most familiar. The sheets of earthen material built over vegetation that is being eaten are others. Some desert termites are known to build vertical tunnels deep into the soil to locate a source of moisture for the colony. Some species build special structures evidently designed to keep excessive rain off their arboreal nests. One such structure consists of chevron-shaped wedges built to deflect water from a nest located below the wedges on the side of a tree. Another consists of semicircular caps built above a nest in the same type of location. Nests on the ground may even be capped, so that the whole resembles a large mushroom, the cap serving as an umbrella. There are even termites that construct with their building materials, not covered runways, but "paved" roads over which the foragers travel.

While the usual concept of termites is that of wood eaters and wood dwellers, we have seen that as a group they use many other items as their food supply and for their nesting sites. Plant materials of all sorts, from cellulose to fungi, provide their nourishment. Even meat may occasionally enter their diet through cannibalism—a dead or dying nest mate often being eaten—and through the digestion of dead protozoa within the intestinal tracts of the wood eaters. Nor do the termites suffer from any human-type qualms about the methods by which they obtain their nourishment. Depending on the ability of their mouthparts, the majority of the termites in a colony will eat food whether it consists of bits rasped from plant growth, liquid offerings from the mouth or anus of another, nibbles of fungi growing on the walls or on fecal pellets dropped or spread on the floors or walls, or tasty exudates derived by licking the eggs or the bodies of nymphs, workers, or soldiers, or most especially by licking the body of the queen. And from this food a portion of the termites' building material is often derived, as a salivary secretion and/or as excrement. The termites have developed a highly involved society based on a parsimonious economy.

Epilogue: Relationships

NEITHER WASP, BEE, ant, termite, or man lives in isolation. All live in relationship to other living things about them. And because these insects and man have attained a social level wherein large numbers of a species live and work together, they are, by sheer bulk of numbers and by efficient organization of those numbers, particularly influential in, and often significantly affected by, the relationships developed between them and their environment. These relationships are innumerable.

Many of the social insects are taken advantage of by parasitic species of their own type. We noted the cuckoo species of wasps and bumblebees, which enter the nest of a closely related species and lay their eggs there, depending on the host workers to raise their young for them. Only a very few species of parasitic termites are known and their parasitic way of life has only rather recently been discovered. We have discussed the various stages of parasitism of ants by others of their kind, and this parasitic way of life, as exhibited on a variety of levels of dependency, is particularly pronounced among the flexible and adaptable ants.

The nests of the social insects provide inviting quarters for creatures besides those building them. Just as man's homes, despite all he can do to prevent it, may be home sites for everything from mice to cockroaches to flies, so the homes of the social insects are besieged by a wide variety of pests. And, just as man often keeps in his home animal guests, such as dogs and cats, so do some of the social insects purposely keep guests in theirs. Food, warmth, shelter from the weather, and a measure of protection from enemies are available to those small creatures which can adjust their lives to living with their hosts. So well have they succeeded that there are several thousand such creatures known today to be living with ants alone. These are known as myrmecophiles, meaning "ant-lovers." A lesser number are known from termite nests and these are called termitophiles. Fewer guests are found among the wasps and bees, but these too have creatures that live in or on them, or in their nests. Guests of the social insects range from creatures that are persecuted by the hosts to those that are tolerated or ignored to those that are actually desired. Only the ants and termites truly keep guests—that is, have those that are desired by their hosts.

The hives of honeybees may harbor a variety of creatures living in cracks and crevices, eating debris or stealing honey and wax. Two of these are the wax moth and the bee louse. A particularly damaging resident in some hives is the larva of the wax moth. The female moth enters a hive and there lays her eggs. The larvae that develop have a healthy appetite for wax and literally eat their way through the comb. They also feed on other material they find as they move through the combs. They leave behind messy webs, excrement, ruined comb, and eventually a destroyed colony.

The so-called bee louse plagues the honeybees, particularly the queens. These insects are really flies that long ago lost their wings after their adoption of a parasitic way of life. They crawl about in the bee's fur and when desiring food move to the bee's mouth, where they help themselves when drops of food are being passed from one bee to another. The louse may even solicit food by touching the bee's mouth in such a manner that the bee is duped into regurgitating food, probably mistaking the food request for one made by another bee.

The ants, living in such a variety of locations and following so many different living patterns, provide many niches into which other creatures can fit and proceed to live successfully. It is among the ants that we find some of the most interesting of the guests of the social insects. Ant homes are inhabited by many small creatures that obtain a variety of types of food from their hosts. Some guests simply scavenge for refuse. Others may steal food, and among these are certain small mites which attach themselves to the ants' bodies. If close to the ant's head, the mite will stroke the ant, inducing her to regurgitate food to it, or steal food during a food exchange between ants. Those more unfortunate mites that are attached elsewhere on the ant's body solicit the mouths of ants which are standing close to it, or steal food from an exchange taking place nearby. Ants' eggs, larvae, pupae, and adult ants are eaten by various guests. Body secretions are licked from the ants' bodies by other guests, including unusual diminutive wingless crickets. A small wingless roach, *Attaphila fungicola,* lives only in the nests of *Atta texana,* a leaf cutter, and is a scavenger there. It also follows the odor trails laid by the *Atta* ants, probably as a means of moving to new nests. In addition, some of the tiny roaches attach themselves to virgin queens leaving on their mating flights and so are carried into the new nests with the queens. Pellets discarded from the ants' infrabuccal chambers, ant excreta, material from the ants' cleaning organs, and even body exudates on the walls of the nest serve as guest food. And finally some guests have food handed—or rather mouthed—directly to them by the ants, receiving drops of regurgitated food directly from their hosts. Little, if anything, goes to waste.

These guests, uninvited or invited, have often become well adapted for this way of life. Some of them use mimicry—that is, they closely resemble the ants. This may trick the ants into believing that these are other ants or trick predators into thinking these creatures are really ants, thus providing protection for the impostors. There are even spiders which live with ants and mimic them in appearance. Spiders have eight legs and ants have six. The mimics simply elevate and wave their extra pair of front legs to imitate antennae, which they do not have but need in order to look like ants. There are residents in ant nests that have a special body form which aids them in slipping away from the ants. Some are so tiny that they easily escape from the larger ants. Others may have hard, protective body coverings, or be equipped with an offensive spray. The most extreme in their adaptation and the most interesting are the true myrmecophiles. These are usually beetles which have tufts of golden hairs called trichomes on their bodies. Through these are discharged glandular secretions that are prized by the ants. Since we know that many of the ants are fond of licking one another and obtaining exudates, it is easy to see that their gustatory greed can lead them to enjoying secretions from other insects—indeed, that is what they are doing when they obtain honeydew from aphids. Just how far astray this desire can lead them is seen, however, when ants such as *Formica sanguinea* keep as a guest a beetle of the genus *Lomechusa.* Through their trichomes, the beetles provide a secretion for the ants, which is eagerly imbibed. The beetles request regurgitated food from the ants and this is given them. Thus far it is a fair trade. The beetle larvae are evidently attractive to the ants or know the correct method of soliciting food, for these too are fed regurgitated food by the ants, but in addition the larvae eat the ant brood! The drain of feeding the adult beetles and their larvae, plus the loss of a portion of the ant brood to these guests, can in time seriously weaken an ant colony, the members of which have stomachs bigger than their eyes, for they are physically incapable of seeing beyond their own gustatory desires. They have no ability to discern cause and effect. Such examples of exploitation are not uncommon among ants, and in the ant world there are a good many guests who come to dinner and stay to eat their hosts' children.

The ants' and the termites' societies are similar in so many ways it is not surprising that the termites too act as hosts for a large population of scavengers, thieves, pests, and guests of many types. As with the ants, it is the more advanced termites that support the greater variety and number of these creatures, have guests that are actually desired and guests that have bodily forms especially adapted for the life they lead.

The termites' special guests are those that produce from glands or appendages exudates desired by the termites; these include members of the fly, moth, and beetle groups of insects. An unusual condition that occurs among some of these desired guests is the great distention of the guest's abdomen. This enlargement may possibly be caused by these special guests' receiving the same food as the queen, who is also often greatly enlarged.

Many of these remarkable relationships between ants and their guests, and termites and theirs, have been in existence for millions of years. The guests have had a great deal of time in which to evolve body forms and behavior patterns that fit them for the role they play. So adapted are they for the life they now lead that most of them could not survive without the host, and in some cases the host also desires the association. As a result, many of the relationships are so strong that we find such situations as an ant colony migrating with its guests migrating right along with it. Some guests make the trip under their own power, but others are carried to the new home by their hosts. The sizes of the participants are different, but much the same situation is found in our human society, for man has been taking dogs with him to new home sites for a good many years, and the dogs have been evolving (with the active help of man) to fit better into this relationship, until today many breeds of dogs are far different from the basic stock from which they started.

The relationships of the social insects with living things about them, in addition to their specific guests, are myriad and on many levels, ranging from neutral to predator to prey. Many volumes could be written on these subjects alone. We find such strange examples as a toad which lives with the primitive ponerine ant, *Myrmecia regularis*. The toad is a very small one which lives under logs or rocks, moving about slowly looking for insects to eat. These toads have been found numerous times living in the nests of these fierce, stinging ants. They feed upon small insects that gather in the ants' nest, drawn by refuse. The toads move about in the nest, even among the brood, but evidently do not eat the ants or their young. The ants for their part mainly ignore the toad; they may crawl about over it but do not harm it. Neither toads nor ants are dependent upon one another; each can live alone, but together each probably helps the other to some extent.

The termites also have their strange visitors, their homes sometimes being invaded by creatures that usurp a part for themselves without destroying the termite colony. Thus there are reported certain ants that take over parts of termite carton nests for their quarters, the termites and ants each living amicably in their own portions of the duplex; birds that excavate their nests in arboreal termite nests; and stingless-bee colonies that build their homes within a portion of a termite's nest.

Certain insects which may or may not interact directly with the social insects derive benefit from them. For example, there are insects that mimic the bumblebees and through their appearance deceive predators. One of these is a robber fly. This mimic has developed a fuzzy, plump, beelike body, hairy legs, and a color pattern resembling the bumblebee model. It even has two areas of light hair on the hind legs to resemble the bumblebees' pollen baskets. In experiments, toads that had tried to eat bumblebees and been stung by them and thereafter avoided eating bumblebees, also avoided eating the robber flies, considering these to be more bumblebees, although the robber flies have no stings and would not have harmed the toads had they tried to eat them. In addition it was found that whenever possible the mimics pounced on bumblebees and ate them. Their resemblance to the bumblebees apparently gave them an advantage in that they were able to approach the bees more easily than if they had been greatly different in form and color. The mimicking of bumblebees by the robber flies would therefore appear to give these robber flies the double advantage of protection from predators and increased ease in preying upon the bees.

Other flies mimic wasps, and it was a drone fly that mimics the honeybee which caused the belief that honeybees could be spontaneously generated from the carcass of a dead ox. This fly breeds in putrid organic matter; so flies, rather than bees, did indeed come from the ox, but not by spontaneous generation.

The social insects are preyed upon by many creatures and form an important food item in the interconnected web of animal life. Ants are the greatest enemies of the termites, and, as has often been said, ants are the greatest enemies of other ants. Army ants invade wasp colonies and devour the brood, and the adult wasps must then start their labors again. Conversely there is a wasp which specializes in stocking its underground nests with harvester ants.

There are large animals specialized to feed on ants and termites and these include some of the strangest of the earth's creatures, such as the echidnas, or spiny anteaters, primitive Australian mammals; African aardvarks; armadillos; and pangolins, or scaly anteaters, in addition to bears. The pangolin is covered with large, overlapping, protective scales. Its snout is long and pointed. With powerful claws it rips into an ant nest and catches the ants by flicking out its very long sticky tongue into their masses and quickly retracting the tongue into its mouth, where the ants are raked off, swallowed, and finally ground up in the anteater's stomach. These animals, in addition to their body scales and heavy eyelids, have nostrils and ear openings that can be closed, all as protection against the ants. By rolling themselves up into a tight ball, they are protected by their scales from larger animals.

Reptiles and amphibians are known to eat great quantities of ants and termites. There are African lizards which follow the driver ants, grab mouthfuls of them from a swarm, and then swiftly retire to eat their catch. Our American horned "toads," or lizards, eat large numbers of ants. One was observed eating ninety-one large *Pogonomyrmex* ants in an hour. The lizards do not seem to be disturbed by the stinging ability of the ants, which they swiftly procure with a flick of their tongue and with equal speed swallow whole. Frogs and toads also eat vast numbers of ants and termites.

Termites in the alate stage are more susceptible to these predators, but some reptiles evidently also eat them underground. A small Mexican blind snake has recently been reported as feeding in captivity on termites. Ant pupae given it caused no reaction, but it fed freely on termite workers placed in its quarters. Its method of doing so was most unusual, for it always approached the termite from the posterior end, even if it had to move about to do so. The termite was grasped in the snake's jaws, which worked themselves up to the termite's head. The termite was then ejected from the snake's mouth, its abdomen collapsed and empty.

Insects of many kinds prey upon the social insects, one of the best known being the ant lion. This insect larva catches ants and other small insects in its conical pit in the sand or dust. The larva lies at the bottom of the pit. Busy, wandering ants often fall into these miniature cones and because of the shape of the pit and the loose dust are unable to climb back out. They drop to the bottom, are pierced by the mouthparts of the larva there, and so are eaten. Bees and wasps are attacked by insects that await them on the flowers.

Birds, too, take a large toll of the social insects. Ants form a high percentage of the food of some species of birds, and the winged forms of termites are eaten by them in enormous quantities when they are swarming. Other interesting relationships exist between birds and some social insects. There are birds which regularly follow the raiding driver ants and

Lurking among the flowers are animals which prey upon the bees who come there to gather nectar and pollen. A humanly grotesque praying mantis here devours a bumblebee it has caught. A male mantis clings to the hungry female's back.

legionary ants, usually not to prey on the ants but rather to capture some of the insects flushed out of hiding by the ants. A remarkable relationship is that of a bird called the African honey guide to certain mammals. Here the relationship is not directly with a social insect but is dependent upon one, for the honey guide is interested in beeswax. There are several species of these small birds which, on finding a nest of wild bees, go in search of a human being or a mammal known as a honey badger. If the bird finds such an individual it alights nearby and begins to chatter. If the listener responds, the bird flies in the direction of the bees' nest, stops, chatters, and waits. If the bird is successful in this procuring of help, the individual called upon breaks open the nest, a feat of which the bird is incapable, and takes or eats the honey. The honey guide is not interested in the honey but in the wax. Once the bird's helper leaves, the bird will feed on the exposed comb and brood. These birds contain peculiar intestinal bacteria that aid them in digesting the usually indigestible wax. In the native African tribes superstitions about these birds abound, one of these being that if such a bird calls you and you refuse to open the hive for it, the next time it calls you it will lead you to a lion or poisonous snake.

Man in the past has eaten the social insects and continues to do so today. They have also played a part in his medicine, folklore, and justice through torture for countless centuries. For food man has often consumed honey ants; eaten large, swarming queens of various species—either raw or cooked, whole or portions; flavored cake icings with formicine ants; distilled ants with rye for added flavor in brandy; mashed ants into a paste to eat with curry or to be added to water for a drink. Some tribes of men gather and eat the large female termite alates when these swarm, and some have various chants and other measures used supposedly to induce the swarming. Even the clay of certain African termite nests is reported to be chewed by natives. Medicinally, the eating of queen termites is supposed to invigorate old men; ant diets have been used to treat scurvy; the heads of ants have been used to hold wounds together, the jaws being clamped shut on the two edges to close the incision; and formic acid from ants has been added to bath water as a remedy for rheumatism and gout. Among many primitive people ants were used to torture enemies and unfaithful wives, and they were also oftentimes used in puberty and endurance rites. And if these uses seem strange, let us add that the most modern way of eating ants is found at fashionable cocktail parties where the ants are served with chocolate coatings!

While the rather curious uses of social insects by man are of interest, they do not represent the real importance of these insects to him. Bees are of vital significance to both the plant and animal world as some of the most effective agents of pollination of plants. Man now sprays his crops with deadly insecticides, which succeed not only in killing noxious insects, but also are having a serious detrimental effect on the vitally necessary agents of pollination, the honeybees. The bees are important as producers of honey and wax and have been an integral part of man's life since the Stone Age. Wasps and ants are very important as predators of other insects. In several European countries, certain ants are protected by law, government agencies transplant colonies of them, and active research programs are carried on in successful efforts to use ants as biological controls against noxious forest insects. Ants are probably of greater significance as soil movers than the widely acclaimed earthworms, for ants are found in wide areas over the earth where earthworms do not even occur, and the soil-moving activity of the ants is remarkable due to their individual ability and the vast numbers of them present. We have noted that termites are of great value, particularly in the tropics. They are among the relatively few creatures that can break wood down into the basic elements to be used again in the never-ending cycle of life, growth, death, and life. The social insects are also of significance in a negative way. Certainly the home owner who finds his house infested by termites, the farmer whose land sprouts hard mounds of introduced stinging fire ants, the agriculturist who finds his tropical trees stripped by leaf-cutting ants, or simply the gardener who bumbles into a wasps' nest are understandably vehement about their dislike for particular social insects. The social insects, little upon the earth but numerous, are, however, a vital part of the life on our planet.

Perhaps it is in the relationships of the social insects within a species, among allied species, and with species of completely different living things that one of their great values to man lies. Man is so large, so numerous, and so effective that he has often destroyed relationships between himself and his environment, or between elements in his environment, before he has become aware of these relationships, or aware of the results of his actions, or before he has developed the conscience to refrain from these actions. He continues to do so today. Perhaps the small worlds of the social insects can provide man with a miniature view and a greatly needed understanding of the interrelatedness, interdependency, complexity, and wonder of living things.

Index